COSMIC ARCHITECTURE IN INDIA

Andreas Volwahsen

COSMIC ARCHITECTURE IN INDIA

The Astronomical Monuments
of Maharaja Jai Singh II

Prestel   Munich · London · New York

Mapin Publishing   Ahmedabad

The author is grateful to Nina Gembrys
and Sandra Beinvogel for their work
constructing the shadows and colour
effects on the plans in this book.

Front jacket see pp. 80–81
Back jacket see p. 53
Half-title see note 59 p. 82
Frontpapers © Collection of Dietmar Siegert
Frontispiece and Endpapers see pp. 68–69

Prestel-Verlag
Mandlstrasse 26 · D-80802 Munich GERMANY
Tel.: (89) 38-17-09-0 · Fax.: (89) 38-17-09-35
www.prestel.de

4 Bloomsbury Place · London WC1A 2QA
Tel.: (020) 73 23 5004 · Fax.: (020) 76 36 8004

175 Fifth Avenue, Suite 402 · New York NY 10010
Tel.: (212) 9 95 27 20 · Fax.: (212) 9 95 27 33
www.prestel.com

Mapin Publishing Pvt. Ltd.
Chidambaram, Ahmedabad 380013 INDIA
mapin@icenet.net
www.mapinpub.com

Library of Congress Control Number: 200 109 2004

Prestel books are available worldwide.
Please contact your nearest bookseller or
any of the above addresses for information
concerning your local distributor.

Translated from the German by Sandra Harper
Editorial direction: Philippa Hurd
Editing: Bernard Wooding
Designed and typeset by Cilly Klotz

Origination by ReproLine, Munich
Printed by Gerstmayer, Weingarten
Bound by Conzella, Pfarrkirchen

Printed in Germany on acid-free paper

ISBN 3-7913-2506-X (Prestel)
ISBN 81-85822-87-5 (Mapin)

Contents

Introduction

Little research has been carried out on the architecture of India. As a result, Western observers tend to approach it with amazement rather than understanding. Hindu temples elude attempts to recognise the true shape embedded in their sumptuous embellishments of mythological figures and abstract symbolic sculptures. To Western eyes, Muslim mosques, tombs and palaces seem like theatrical conglomerations of pointed arches and onion towers built from precious stones and jewels, but their architectural structure is incomprehensible.

Along with the agents of English colonial power, European historians and architects flocked to India and set about classifying the country's historic buildings into styles. In the 19th century, a time when art historians were intent on cataloguing everything and establishing a comprehensive network of stylistic periods, there was great interest in the wealth of forms discovered in India. Also, for Western architects enamoured of eclecticism, the country provided a vast gateway to a world of magnificent new architectural forms.

During this period, however, people overlooked one of the great achievements of Indian architecture: the observatories built by Maharaja Jai Singh II of Jaipur (1686–1743) in Delhi, Jaipur, Benares, Ujjain and Mathura. Known by the name of Jantar Mantar (see glossary), these escaped the notice of the art experts because they did not appear to fit in anywhere, and they were ignored by the practitioners of eclectic architecture because their lack of decoration provided little stimulation to the imagination.

Even today Westerners tend to approach Indian architecture with preconceptions, and consequently an encounter with Jai Singh's buildings comes as a wonderful surprise. To begin with, these monumental stone cubes with their concave and convex shapes, together with the broad marble scales up which steps ascend, have nothing in common with the splendid architecture of the Mogul period. Furthermore, for the present-day viewer these structures conjure up the curious image of a brilliant 18th-century architect playing ironic games with architectural notions of form and function. Such a notion is absurd, of course. And yet the fact that these remote and isolated monuments, partly decayed beyond recognition, do not conform to the manifestos and preconceived ideas of our age certainly provides food for thought.

How did these enormous sculptures come to be built? Was their construction preceded by some particular development in architectural theory which was repeated two centuries later, leading to comparable forms? Or is our instinctive understanding of the beauty of the observatories of North India basically a misunderstanding?

An encounter with the gigantic astronomical instruments of Jai Singh II prompts us to ask questions about the specific cultural conditions prevailing at the time and about the architect's conception of science. Why did Jai Singh and his astronomers design marble measuring scales taller than all the surrounding palace buildings? They were familiar with the small European and Arabian instruments with their accurate sighting equipment. They were also familiar with the telescope which had been known in Europe since the days of Galileo (1564–1642). Jesuits on their travels brought these instruments to the court in Jaipur, and Jai Singh would doubtless have tested them out.

In his text *Zig Muhammad Shahi,* Jai Singh himself answers these questions: 'It should be maintained that these instruments [of the Europeans] were not large and, therefore, the calculation and observations were somewhat inaccurate, since the atmospheric conditions had a strong influence on those instruments; we explained that the inadequate accuracy of the observatories and measurements by Hipparchus, Ptolemy and others particularly indicated this.'

With the benefit of hindsight, his decision to use large fixed instruments without the sighting equipment appropriate to the current state of technology seems to us today to have more to do with Hindu philosophy: portrayals of the cosmos and the world of the gods confer on the expert knowledge of and power over this world far beyond the information they provide. Jai Singh was not merely commissioning his Hindu priest-architects to design his new royal capital of Jaipur according to the geometric framework of a Hindu mandala. Through these astronomical instruments or tools of a cosmic order, which were visible from a great distance, he was also underlining his claim to worldly power.

Jai Singh's decision to build a town as a mandala, with the earth as its centre, and to construct observatories as yantras, with the cosmos as a frame of reference, were his answer to the late period of Mogul rule in India, which was characterised by wars and decadence.

At the beginning of the 18th century, the successors of the Great Mogul Aurangzeb drove out and murdered one another in quick succession. English trade bases were established with their own claim to power. And the Persian Nadir Shah finally conquered the Mogul empire in 1739. As prince of the region, Jai Singh was directly involved in all this upheaval and confusion. His alternative plan for a world marked by science and universal principles of order confirms his outstanding importance in the history of architecture and town planning in India.

The desire to locate human behaviour in a higher framework – whether religious or scientific – is the mark of all cultures. To understand the path chosen by Jai Singh, it is illuminating to study earlier examples from different cultures. The pyramids in Egypt, the stone circles at Stonehenge, the temples of the Maya and the castles of the Dane Tycho Brahe are all characterised by the same desire to bring architecture and the cosmos into a comprehensible relationship by means of astronomy.

Our very sketchy knowledge about the life and person of Jai Singh makes it impossible for us to put forward a conclusive thesis on the factors which led to the planning and construction of the observatories in Jaipur, Delhi, Benares, Ujjain and Mathura. In a comparably poor principality in Rajasthan, in an age marked by conflicts between the Hindu princes and the Islamic ruling house of the Mogul emperors, within the course of a few years some monumental buildings were built which were free from the Islamic architectural style of the age and full of references to Hindu cosmology.

Finally, and most amazing of all, after years of studying all the details, it emerges that at least one of the maharaja's inventions, namely the Mishra Yantra in Delhi, can have had no useful function as a measuring instrument. Here, as in other advanced civilisations, rulers, architects, artists and priests created their own cosmos for themselves.

1 | Precursors and Models

According to what principles of order is the universe built? This is one of the oldest questions asked by mankind. People only rarely asked whether there was any principle of order at all; the belief in an all-embracing order has been the starting point for philosophical and scientific enquiry for thousands of years.

In their quest for an answer, theologians, philosophers and scientists have followed various paths at various times and their findings have varied widely. Only in the field of astronomy had laws already been empirically recognised in the oldest cultures. The apparent diurnal motion of the sun, the movements of the stars and the cycle of the seasons were seen as proof of a universal order. The geometrical determination of the sunrise, meridian transit and sunset led to the four compass points and, with that, the shape of a right-angled cross became the geometrical basis of spatial thinking. From the shape of the cross it was only a small step to the square and finally to the cube, one of the most important architectural forms for many epochs.

The circle, likewise deduced from astronomical observation, together with its spatial counterpart the sphere, also became basic architectural elements. Their use was more limited, however, because they made greater demands technically and conceptually than the cube – it is easier to establish whether a line is straight and an angle right-angled than to check the accuracy of a circle and a sphere.

Thus there are at least two reasons why the cube plays such an important role in architecture. First, it is made up of lines and angles which are visually clear. Second, it is a portrayal of the basic order which, thanks to our knowledge of astronomy, we consider to be a universal spatial law.

Fig. 1 One of the so-called 'sun wheels' at the Hindu sun temple at Konarak, 13th century. The right-angled axes of the compass rose were represented pointing towards the points of the compass and the apparent orbit of the sun.

Even in the theoretical writings of present-day architects, one encounters the demand that a building should correspond to an extensive 'universal' order over and above functional and aesthetic considerations. This order occasionally differs significantly from the aforementioned traditional structure of space. Buckminster Fuller, for example, talking about the propagation of hexagonal and tetrahedronal structures, observed how paradoxical it was for man to attempt to force his experience of his environment into the framework of a cube.[1]

For Fuller, the 'discovery' that many organic and inorganic structures use the 60° angle in their construction was reason for assuming that nature – in the broadest sense – basically uses triangles, hexagons and tetrahedrons as its

1 Buckminster Fuller, *Structure in Art and Science*, Vision and Value series, Studio Vista, London, 1965.

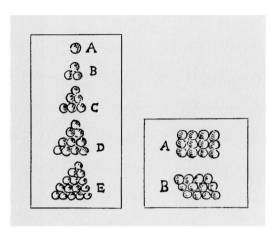

Fig. 2 Johannes Kepler was the first person to carry out geometrical analysis of the tightest possible way to pack spheres.

Fig. 3 Buckminster Fuller and Arthur Loeb opposed the traditional rectangular coordinate system with the tetrahedral structure derived from the tightest possible way of packing spheres.

smallest modules. In his architecture, Fuller rejected the traditional 'trihedral' (X-, Y-, Z-plane), astronomically-oriented conception of space, in favour of the principle of the 'tetrahedron', in which the right-angle is replaced by the 60° angle.

In his search for the original energy structure of the universe, Fuller, while observing the most compact way to pack spheres, hit upon the hexagon (for the most compact arrangement in one plane) and the tetrahedron (for the most compact spatial arrangement). He deduced the so-called energetic and synergetic geometry from the tetrahedronal grid, which led on the one hand to such fanciful technical inventions as his geodesic domes and, on the other hand, through speculations about cosmology, to something approaching numerology.

Fuller's 'energetic and synergetic geometry' can actually be seen as a systematic development of theories about the formation of the universe such as those postulated by Johannes Kepler (1571–1630) in his pamphlet on hexagonal snow. In this essay, Kepler employed almost the same words as Fuller and Arthur Loeb:

Rhombic bodies are formed from spheres under pressure (in the most compact ar-rangement possible). This arrangement is very similar to the octahedron and the pyramid. It is the most compact concentration possible: so that there is no other way that any more spheres could be held in the same container.

It is not surprising, therefore, that Fuller also created in his new geometry a counterpart to the 'five regular bodies' (fig. 111) on which Kepler's 'mystery of the world' was based. Here, too, geometrical and arithmetical laws were given universal validity over and above their limits – further testimony to man's desire to define his environment in terms of geometrical structure, whether it be tetrahedronal, cubic, or, as in India, mainly Tantric (fig. 108).

The combination of astronomical knowledge with formal theories is detectable in the art and architecture of all cultures, but only rarely does one encounter buildings which themselves were used as astronomical devices. Although elementary astronomical knowledge abstracted as a geometric concept formed the starting point and the precondition for many architectural designs, astronomy rarely served as a reason in itself for building.

2 'Let a marble slab be fixed level in the centre of the space enclosed by the walls, or let the ground be smoothed and levelled, so that the slab may not be necessary. In the centre of this plane, for the purpose of marking the shadow correctly, a brazen gnomon must be erected. The Greeks call this gnomon skiathe'ras. The shadow cast by the gnomon is to be marked about the fifth ante-meridional hour, and the extreme point of the shadow accurately determined. From the central point of the space whereon the gnomon stands, as a centre, with a distance equal to the length of the shadow just observed, describe a circle. After the sun has passed the meridian, watch the shadow which the gnomon continues to cast till the moment when its extremity again touches the circle which has been described.' Vitruvius, *De Architectura*, translated by Joseph Gwilt, book 1, chapter 6, London, 1826.

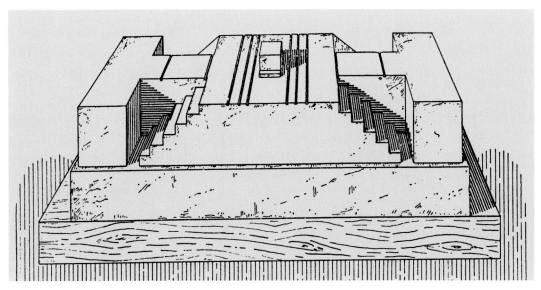

Fig. 4 This small stone sundial from Egypt represents three different monumental sundials.

It is possible to divide buildings into various groups according to their relationship to astronomy:

1. Buildings with a clear-cut astronomical purpose, such as the Egyptian obelisks, Stonehenge in England or Jai Singh's observatories in northern India.
2. Buildings which were designed as a result of astronomical or cosmological ideas, for example the astronomer Tycho Brahe's Uraniborg Castle, the domed buildings of Christianity and Islam, and examples of town planning such as the Roman castrum or the classical Chinese town.
3. Buildings which merely adopt the geometrical canon arising from early astronomy (right-angled buildings).
4. Buildings which do not conform to the X-Y-Z coordinate system, for example Asiatic bamboo buildings or Buckminster Fuller's domes.

Egypt

The obelisks and pyramids may both have belonged to the first group. It is well known that the purpose of the obelisks was to cast a shadow and thereby serve as a sundial. The length of the shadow showed the time of day and the bisector

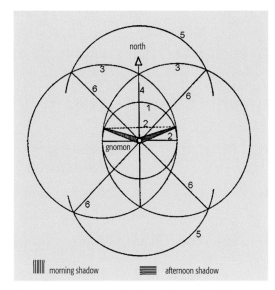

Fig. 5 In Egypt, Rome and ancient India, a pole which cast shadows (gnomon) was used to establish north.

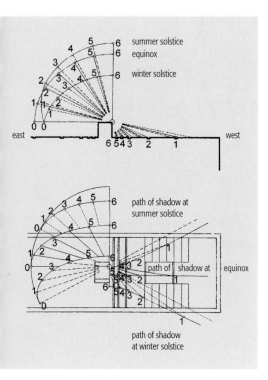

Fig. 6   Geometrical analysis of a sundial with a horizontal face: top, vertical section; bottom, top view.

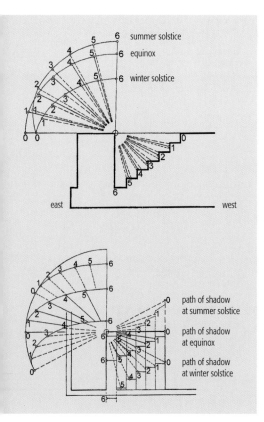

Fig. 7   Geometrical analysis of a sundial with stepped face: top, vertical section; bottom, top view.

of an angle between a shadow recorded in the morning and one recorded in the afternoon pointed north. The bisector of the angle was presumably obtained according to a process described later by Vitruvius.[2] In order to increase the accuracy of the measurements, they fixed a metal spike on to the top of the obelisk. Its top was shaped like a small sphere and it cast a clearly defined shadow.

The extremely precise orientation of the Cheops pyramid (c. 2650 BC) on the four main compass points could certainly not be obtained by finding north from the shadow of a gnomon. In this and similar cases they used a procedure which was as simple as it was intelligent, and which demanded no complicated astronomical instruments. The discovery of a plumb line and a palm rib[3] with a notch made it possible to reconstruct the procedure. The way these worked is indicated in several reliefs.

Establishing the axis of a temple or pyramid was one of the tasks of the king. In one hand, he held the palm rib vertically up to his eyes, and in the other hand, with his arm outstretched, he held the plumb line. In this way he could observe any direction he wanted through the notch and the plumb line and get an assistant to place one or several ranging rods in this sighting line by directing him to one side or the other, until the ranging rod, plumb line and notch were aligned. If north-south was to be determined, as in the building of the Cheops pyramid or the Re shrine in Abu Gurôb (2500 BC),[4] then the king would twice observe over an artificial horizon any star lying as close as possible to the pole, once as it set and once as it rose. They marked its rising and setting points with ranging rods and halved the angle between the two directions.[5] This method was developed before the fifth dynasty (from 2563 BC). The oldest building whose precise orientation on the four compass points can only be explained by north being fixed in this way is the pyramid of King Snofru at Medûm (c. 2700 BC).

We have no intention of adding yet another theory to the existing ones about the origin and symbolism of the pyramids. An experiment in 1853[6] had already shown that it would have been an easy thing for the Egyptian priests to use the Cheops pyramid to establish the equinoxes, if they observed the sunrise and sunset over the edges of the pyramid. The maximum deviation of a base edge is 0°5'30" (eastern edge), the minimum deviation 0°1'57" (southern edge).[7]

It is no less surprising that a passage leading from north to south into the pyramid's underground burial chamber was built at an angle of 26°18'. This angle corresponds exactly to the geographical latitude of the pyramid. The corridor runs parallel to the earth's axis. As a result, the Cheops pyramid contains all the directions necessary for astronomical measurement. However, the sloping corridor was walled up after the death of Cheops and as a result the pyramid could no longer be used as an instrument for observing the universe. The astronomical orientation was therefore presumably primarily of symbolic value.

At no time in Egyptian history were there any fixed observatories which might have been used regularly for observing the sky. Measurements were carried out when necessary by the priests in the temples. Apart from the obelisks, they used many different kinds of small sundials for this. One of these was a small stone sundial whose architectural form reflects the monumental conception of Egyptian temple sites. According to Borchardt,[8] who studied this white limestone sundial in depth, it was actually an architectural model depicting three different kinds of monumental sundials in miniature – a record of the development of a timekeeper as it appeared possible at that time (figs. 4, 6 and 7).

Before we look more closely at this model, we should cast a quick glance at the division of time. It was the task of all sundials simply to divide the day into twelve hours. There is no mention in any writings of smaller units of time, such as half

Fig. 8   The triangular sides of the Cheops pyramid near Cairo point in the direction of the four points of the compass and the passage leading to the king's burial chamber runs parallel to the earth's axis.

3   Berlin Mus. no. 14084/5.

4   Berlin Mus. no. 20080.

5   According to Maxence de Rochemonteix and Emile Chassinat (*Le temple d'Edfou,* 1987, p. 31), in an inscription in Edfu it says that the king, during the sacred act, says, 'I take the ranging rod, hold the end of the stick and grasp the string together with the goddess of wisdom. I turn my face towards the path of the star. I turn my eyes towards the constellation of the Little Bear. The Sk-'h'w (god Thot) stands by his measuring instrument (merchet). I establish the four corners of the temple.'

6   See description in Jean-Baptiste Biot, 'Détermination de l'Équinoxe vernal de 1853', in *Astronomie égyptienne,* Paris, 1855.

7   According to Ludwig Borchardt, *Längen und Richtungen der vier Grundkanten der Grossen Pyramide bei Gise,* Berlin, 1926.

8   Ludwig Borchardt, 'Alte ägyptische Zeitmessung', in *Geschichte der Zeitmessung und der Uhren,* Berlin, 1920.

hours or even minutes. The word 'hour' can be traced back to around 3000 BC, but the length of an hour was only a very imprecise measurement of time since they divided the short winter days into twelve hours in just the same way as the long summer days. They also often preferred a division of the day calculated from dusk to dusk, rather than from sunrise to sunset. A different measurement of time resulted from this again.

The examination of the limestone model shows the difficulties the Egyptians had to face in their attempts to divide this or that measurement of the day into twelve sections of time. The three sundials depicted are:

a) a sundial with a horizontal face, on the upper side of the stone block

b) a sundial with a step-shaped face

c) a sundial with an oblique face

From the symmetry of the model, we can see that the sundial was orientated east-west in its longitudinal direction.

The sundial with a horizontal face (a) consists of a cuboid which casts a shadow, and to the west and east of this, five hour lines on each side on the horizontal plane. An examination of the division of the hours in relation to the geographical latitude for which the sundial was made shows that it was intended to make a precise division of

Fig. 9 *A relief from the Amada Temple, c. 1450 BC, built by Thutmoses III. It shows the king and the goddess Sechat driving in poles to determine the direction of the temple on the basis of astronomical observations.*

the day from sunrise to sunset possible at any time of year. At the equinoxes, however, the second and the eleventh hour are shown as being too long and the third and the tenth hour as too short, because of the incorrect positioning of line no. 2 at the start of the steps. At every other time of year the deviations are much greater. In the diagram (fig. 6), the path of the shadow is also drawn in for the times of the solstices.

The difficulties in producing a horizontal sundial appear to be insuperable, and that is why they presumably tried to make a face in the shape of a staircase (fig. 7). The basic idea behind this construction was that the uniform course of the sun projecting over the edge of a shadow on to a uniformly rising staircase would make a uniform division of the hours possible. And so for morning measurements they built steps inclined to the east and for afternoon measurements steps inclined to the west. Each staircase has six steps corresponding to the way they wanted to divide up the hours.

But the stepped sundial also turns out to be unsuitable for dividing the day into equal portions of time. Its design is based on an architectural shape and not on the knowledge of the geometrical regularity of the (apparent) course of the sun. Thus, in our search for building forms which are determined by their astronomical function, we come across the reverse: existing building shapes influencing astronomical ideas.

The shortcomings of the stepped sundial become apparent with geometrical analysis. We can see that even at the time of the equinoxes the steps could not have been of an equally large size. There are two reasons for this. Firstly, the steps of a uniformly rising staircase produce unequal angles with the edge of the shadows; and secondly, the sun also produces unequal hour angles with the edge of the shadow, since the course of the sun does not lie in the plane of the prime vertical.

A staircase-shaped sundial could be constructed for the equinox if all the treads and risers were of different lengths. But if the sundial is also used at other times of the year, then the edges would have to be curved. But there is no evidence that such a difficult sundial to produce was ever made, either in Egypt or elsewhere.

In a symmetrical position to the staircase-shaped sundial in the limestone model, there is a sundial with oblique surfaces. Small permanent markings are visible on these surfaces, suggesting that the Egyptians were trying to avoid the shortcomings of both the horizontal sundial and the staircase-shaped sundial by recording the actual position of the shadow hour by hour with the aid of a water clock point by point – in other words without any preconceived ideas about the presumed geometrical course. The oblique faces were better suited to this kind of plotting than the horizontal plane, since touching intersections, as they occur on the horizontal sundial in the morning and evening, are avoided.

For establishing the time at night, the Egyptians once again used palm ribs and a plumb line,

9 l or i draconis.
10 Ludwig Borchardt, 'Alte ägyptische Zeitmessung', in *Geschichte der Zeitmessung und der Uhren,* Berlin, 1920, p. 59.

Fig. 10 A multitude of sight lines at Stonehenge suggest astronomical connections.

duction of sundials, they used a water clock for marking out the time. As they did not manage to build a reliable sundial with the help of this, the attempt at a stellar clock was also doomed to failure.

It is not known whether the Egyptians were conscious of the imperfections of their ways of measuring time. According to Borchardt, the thought had either 'never even occurred to them, to compare two sundials built on different basic principles as they were working, or, if they had done and therefore noticed the discrepancies, then they did not understand that either one or both the basic principles on which the two sundials being compared were built had to be incorrect.'[10]

Stonehenge

If we search in the past for architectural monuments which can compare with the observatories of Jai Singh in terms of their astronomical purpose and their symbolic cosmological significance, then we can hardly find a more suitable model than that legendary place of ritual worship in England known today as Stonehenge. Around 3100 BC, Stone Age hunters and farmers began to build a huge ritual site which, over the following thousand or so years, was continually altered and completed by summoning up every technical and physical skill imaginable.

Only a few decades ago, archaeologists stood in bewilderment in front of several concentric circles of holes in the ground and a large number of monoliths, likewise arranged in the shape of circles or horseshoes. But they were able to reconstruct the exact order of the building processes and date the individual building periods by radiocarbon dating. The point of this mysterious puzzle, however, remained unexplained because of the lack of any written records. Since

called a 'merchet'. Two observers who sat in the meridian plane – one sitting to the south giving directions to the other in the north until his head was directly under the pole star[9] – observed the meridian transit of certain stars. From a chart of the stars which had been drawn up with the aid of a water clock, they could now deduce which hour of night was beginning when a certain star disappeared behind the notch and plumb line of one or other of the observers. This method did not produce accurate results since, as in the pro-

11 Gerald Hawkins, *Stonehenge Decoded,* New York, 1965. More recent studies heavily criticise his results, but to date no more comprehensive or convincing analysis has been presented.

Fig. 11 Stonehenge, the Neolithic monument in England, may have served as both a place of worship and an observatory, c. 3100–2000 BC.

the 17th century when, on the order of King James I, people began to concern themselves for the first time with finding an explanation for the mystery, countless more or less sensational theories about the origin and the purpose of the Stonehenge stone circles have been bandied around. These efforts culminated in the investigations carried out by astronomer G. S. Hawkins in 1963 and 1964.[11]

Hawkins used the already well-known alignment of the entrance axis with the sunrise on the day of the summer solstice as an opportunity to look for more astronomical links. He fed an IBM 7090 with the directions of sunrise and sunset, and of the moon and the brightest stars for the year 1500 BC. Then he established, again with

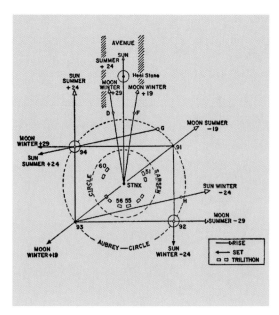

Fig. 12 Overall plan of Stonehenge, c. 3100–2000 BC.

the help of the computer, all the possible alignments between prominent points of the site, such as the tops of the stones or the spaces between them. A comparison of the points at which the sun and moon rose and set with the alignments produced astonishing results. It turned out that there was no link between the alignments and the paths of the stars, but a whole network of

alignments came to light, all pointing to the positions at which the sun and moon rose and set at the equinoxes.

To counter the argument that, given the large number of possible alignments, a handful of suitable lines for any desired direction could be found, a calculation was made for one of the building phases, namely Stonehenge I, as to the likelihood of the correlations being purely coincidental. There is a probability of 0.00006, which means that the chance is smaller than one in ten thousand.

During the first building phase, Stonehenge I, they dug a circular ditch and 56 holes inside the ditch, the so-called Aubrey holes. The ditch was discontinued on the north-east side. In the direction of this entrance, but some 30 metres outside the site, they erected the so-called heel stone and, on the circular line of the Aubrey holes, four so-called 'station stones'. Further stones stood in apparently random positions inside and outside the Aubrey ring. All the stones were unmarked.

The four 'station stones' more or less form a rectangle. The rectangle is, like the axis of the site, formed by the heel stone and the central point of

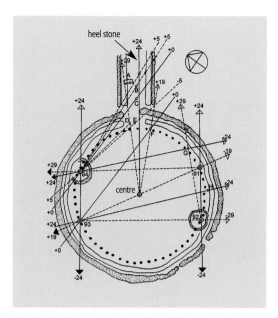

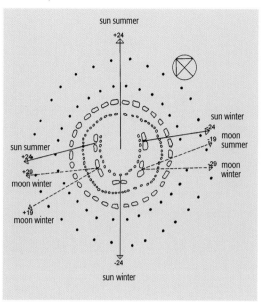

Fig. 13 Sight lines at the observatory of Stonehenge I,
c. 3100 BC.

Fig. 14 Sight lines for Stonehenge III, c. 2000 BC.

the circle, aligned with the point where the sun rises at the summer equinox. Hawkins' investigations showed that almost every alignment between the stones of this building phase pointed to the place where the sun and moon rose and set at the time of the equinoxes and solstices.

There was also an explanation for the 56 earth holes: unusual positions of the full moon, as for example its rise over stones D or F at the winter equinox, are repeated in an 18.61 year cycle. If they succeeded in documenting this cycle over generations in a structural form, then recurrent events which people were afraid of, such as eclipses of the moon and sun, could be predicted.

The priests of Stonehenge presumably wanted to create a circle of holes in the ground for this purpose and to move one or more marked stones on by one hole every year. If they had chosen a circle of 18 or 19 holes, then their predictions of time would have been inaccurate after a few decades. Therefore they decided on a nearly whole-number multiple of 18.61, namely 55.83, and laid out a circle with 56 holes. In this way

the predictions were certain to be sufficiently accurate for a period of several centuries.

In about 2100 BC, the original site was extended. During the Stonehenge II building phase, a double circle of monoliths was built in the centre. Each of the stones – hewn dolerite, rhyolite and volcanic ash – weighs between 4 and 5 tons.

To the amazement of the archaeologists and geologists, it turned out that the monoliths did not come from local quarries but had been transported to Stonehenge from Wales over a distance of 380 kilometres (340 kilometres over water and 40 kilometres over land). For them to go to such trouble, there must have been ritual reasons about which we can only make assumptions. It seems as if they wanted to establish the cycle of the moon with the circle of 37 pairs of stones again. But even as they were building, it was found that choosing to divide the circle into 19 and 18 units would lead to inaccuracies in prediction within the space of a few generations and for this reason the huge building project was abandoned even before the double circle was completed.

In about 2000 BC, new activities at Stonehenge got underway. The double circle was pulled down and a circle of 81 much larger blocks of sandstone erected in its place. Inside that were five enormous archways, so-called trilithons, which consist of two freestanding blocks linked by a lintel. At the same time, the sanctuary was surrounded with 30 giant blocks of sandstone set in a circle and again connected by supports. Inside the trilithons, some of the stones from the former double circle were reerected, but this time in an oval shape. Building in an oval, however, seems – in the same way as the double circle a century earlier – not to have fulfilled the expectations of the architects or priests and that was pulled down again too.

Why go to all this trouble? Like Stonehenge I, Stonehenge III may well have been used for astronomical observation. If we look through one of the trilithons and certain spaces between the stones of the outer sarsen (as these sandstone boulders are known) circle, then we are provided with the same accurate alignments as in Stonehenge I.

The significance of the smaller circle of 81 sarsens is admittedly just as difficult to explain as those built in an oval and subsequently reerected in a horseshoe.

But the alterations were far from being finished. At the same time as they were building the horseshoe, they erected a circle with 59 stones, likewise using the stones from the old double circle. The point of this last extension is easy to see. A lunar month, that is the length of time between two consecutive full moons, is 29.53 days long. If a stone is pushed forwards every day by one unit in a circle with 29 or 30 divisions then one lunar month is too long and one too short. Therefore they erected 59 stones in a circle and now pushed the counting stone forwards by one unit in the evening and one in the morning. In this way the calendar was perfect.

This suggests that every stone and every hole at Stonehenge also had an astronomical or mathematical meaning, in addition to a possible ritual function. The question remains open as to what thoughts could have moved the priests, astronomers and architects of the Stone Age to concentrate the whole energy of their people on a building task that must have been at the extreme limit of what was technically possible. A conservative estimate of all the different tasks in the building of Stonehenge by Hawkins comes to a total cost in time of around 1.5 million man-days, or more than 45,000 man-years!

As in Jai Singh's instruments, those who built Stonehenge went way above the scale of what was absolutely necessary for functional purposes. In this respect, Stonehenge may be yet another example, like Jaipur and Cape Kennedy, of man's desperate desire to overcome space, time and all other conditions of human existence.

Uaxactún, Guatemala, before AD 150

The Maya began systematic astronomical observations in Central America in the first centuries AD in a much less lavish style. From the existing codices, we have to conclude that for fixing their calendar they had some highly developed mathematical knowledge and some precise observation equipment at their disposal. Little is known about the building of the instruments. A few codices admittedly contain illustrations of intersected sighting rods and a head or eye, but only one representation in the Bodleian codex shows the two sights necessary for establishing directions. In the foreground we can see an eye and crossed sighting rods and, in the background, a star which lies just above the V-shaped notch of the second sight (fig. 15).

A detailed reconstruction of the observation methods will only be possible after the Maya script has been fully deciphered. To date we have

Fig. 15 Astronomers and astronomical tools in Mayan codices: a) Nuttall Codex; b) Selden Codex; c) Bodleian Codex.

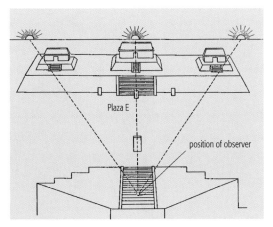

Fig. 16 The observatory in Uaxactún, Guatemala, before AD 150.

Plaza E

position of observer

Copán, Honduras, before AD 900

After the discovery of the observatory of Uaxactún, a dozen more observatories were discovered in all areas of the Maya kingdom, from different centuries and in various shapes.[13] The Copán Valley is the site of an acropolis containing various structures dedicated to the rites of kingship. The Maya erected stelae on top of the mountain ridges on either side of the Copán Valley. These stelae were used by the priests for establishing feast days on which the peasants were supposed to begin burning the harvested

only been able to understand half of some four hundred signs. Results of excavations, however, already permit certain buildings to be identified as observatories.

In Uaxactún, a town which existed in the 4th century AD, Ricketson[12] discovered at 'Plaza E' a pyramid and a group of temples which, because of their particular geometrical arrangement, could be described as an observatory. On the west side of 'Plaza E', a steep staircase leads to the pyramid and on the east side three temples stand on raised platforms. On the day of the summer solstice, from the observation point on the staircase, you can watch the sun rise above the artificial horizon of the platforms exactly along the north-west edge of the north temple. At the winter solstice it rises along the south-west edge of the southern temple and at the time of the equinoxes along the axis of the middle temple (fig. 16).

The observation point is clearly defined by the plaza's east-west axis of symmetry, the plane of the artificial horizon and the sloping plane of the steps. The probability of the situation and orientation of the buildings producing an astronomical alignment by chance is small, and there seems to be no formal or functional reason that would explain this layout.

Fig. 17 Two sites at Copán in Honduras established the direction of the sunrise on a feast day (before AD 900).

fields. The alignment from the east through the west stela in fact points precisely to that point on the horizon at which the sun sets on the 12th April (and on the 7th September), and, according to Morley, is presumably the time set by the priests for the start of the ceremony.[14]

12 Oliver Ricketson, Jr, *The Culture of the Maya*. 1. *Excavation at Uaxactun,* Carnegie Institution of Washington Supp. Publ. no. 6, Washington DC, 1933. Oliver and Edith Ricketson, *Uaxactun, Guatemala, Group E, 1926–1931,* Carnegie Institution of Washington Publ. no. 477, Washington DC, 1937.
13 For example, the tower of the palace in Palenque or the observatory of Maypan (Yukatán).
14 Sylvanus Morley, *The Ancient Maya*, Stanford, 1956.

Fig. 18 The edges of the windows on the upper floor of the large round temple, the Caracol (the snail), at Chichen Itzá served as sight lines for astronomical observations.

Chichen Itzá, Mexico, 10th century AD

In Central America, as in Egypt or India, the observation of the stars lay in the hands of the priests. Astronomy and theology belonged together. The temple was also an observatory and every astronomical activity was assigned a ritual meaning. And so it is not surprising that one of the most beautiful observatories in Central America, the so-called Caracol[15] in Chichen Itzá, built in the 10th century AD, is not merely a functional building but a sprawling architectural complex with wide steps and terraces at different heights. The observation room is barely 4 square metres in size; the terraces for large gatherings of people, on the other hand, extended to around 3,500 square metres.

The observation tower is round – a departure from the usual shape of sacred buildings. It is composed of a cylindrical centre with two circular walls surrounding it concentrically. The orientation of the four doorways on the exterior wall is quite striking in that they point to the four main compass points, since the platform is subordinated to the north-north-east orientation of the whole town.[16] In the heart of the building, a spiral staircase leads into the small rectangular room from where the readings are taken. Three narrow apertures are left open in the thick surrounding walls. From their position and their measurements (fig. 19), we are able to work out how the Maya observed a star: if we look diagonally through one of the openings in such a way that the inside edge of one side of the

15 *Caracol* is Spanish for snail. The name is derived from the spiral staircase inside the building.
16 The reason why town plans are frequently laid out in a north-north-east direction (for example, Uxmal, Chichen Itzá, Palenque and the southern part of Copán) could not be explained until now.

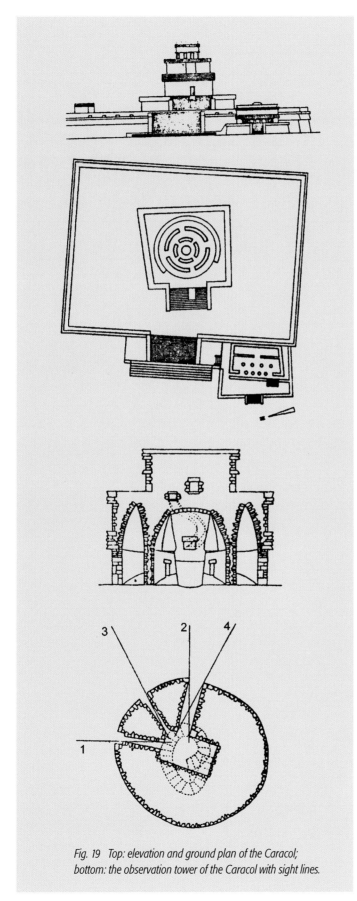

Fig. 19 Top: elevation and ground plan of the Caracol; bottom: the observation tower of the Caracol with sight lines.

window jamb coincides with the external edge of the opposite side, then we are looking in case (1) directly south, in case (2) directly west to the point of the equinoctial sunset, in case (3) at the point of moonset at the vernal equinox and in case (4) at the point of moonset at the summer solstice.

Many different measurements could be taken from this building, since it contained the most important reference planes: the meridian plane and the prime vertical plane. But the Maya were solely interested in establishing the azimuthal directions. No altitudinal markings which might have been displayed on the edges for the comparative measuring of altitudinal angles have been found.

One of the tasks of the observer in the Caracol was presumably to establish noon, that is the time at which the sun casts a first thin streak of light through the south-facing window into the room. But people could also check the calendar from here since the sun, as it sets on the 21st March (or on the 21st September), must already (or is about to) be visible through the west-facing window.

It is no longer possible to draw up a complete list of all the functions of the Caracol because the north-eastern part of the tower has collapsed. Presumably there were more openings for observing the north and the east.

Why did people build such monumental building complexes in Central America or England to determine a few azimuthal directions? Could they not have established them with a small instrument? Are two thin posts anchored a small distance apart as sight markers in the ground or in the stone not enough to mark out a direction with sufficient accuracy?

In Stonehenge, Chichen Itzá and Uaxactún, the priests had recognised that there was only one possibility of reliably defining once and for all the paths of the celestial bodies (precession and nutation were still unknown). They decided to build their sighting instruments and their calendar on such a large scale so that neither individual human strength nor the power of nature would ever destroy the evidence of the recognised order or bring it into disorder. A small-size calculator could easily have been rendered useless by inept handling or hostile intrusion. The giant monoliths of Stonehenge, on the other hand, are still, after almost five thousand years of history, a clear illustration of cosmic order independent of the fate of the people who passed through or settled, ravaged or cultivated this area.

In Central America, too, where they chose to build their observatories on a somewhat less grand scale, it has turned out that even the armies of conquerors and the power of the jungle were not able to destroy completely the heavy stone sighting-axes.

Rome

Things were on a quite different scale in the Mediterranean countries. The Greeks inherited the technical knowledge of Egyptian and Babylonian astronomers and thus had at their disposal the technological capability to produce astronomical instruments which were both easily movable and accurate. They did not channel their astronomical knowledge into megalithic buildings, but rather into a large number of mathematical and astronomical texts which were to influence European, Arabic and Indian astronomy. The theoretical foundations for most of Jai Singh's instruments in India can be traced back to Ptolemy and Hipparchus.

The Greeks, for example, had adopted a type of sundial from the Babylonians, which is also to be found in Jai Singh's observatory, where it is known as the 'Jai Prakash Yantra', or the 'Berossos sundial' (fig. 21). It originally consisted of a hemisphere open at the top and a vertical steel spike, which cast a shadow on to the surface of the hemisphere. This surface can be marked out into hours or, as in Jaipur, Delhi and Benares, into altitudinal and azimuthal divisions (figs. 51, 72, 144, 145).

The Romans adopted a variant of the instrument in which they only used a part of the hemisphere, since the southern part was of little use anyway and only impeded the view into the concave surface.

The Berossos sundial was known and held in high regard as the 'Chamilah' by Arabian astronomers. They added several movable copper measuring circles and a sighting arm with two sights. Jai Singh finally built the Chamilah in monumental architectural form as the Jai Prakash Yantra.

Rei, AD 994

The large stone quadrants of the Shastansha Yantra (see page 48) and the Dakshino Bhitti Yantra (see page 49) in Jaipur are also enlargements of Greek instruments.

Ptolemy was probably the first person to use small, movable quadrants, which were placed in the meridian plane and served to establish

Fig. 21 The sundial designed by Berossos was the model for the Jai Prakash Yantras in the Indian observatories.

the altitudinal or zenithal distance of a celestial body at the time of its meridian transit.

The Ptolemaic quadrant was improved by medieval Arab astronomers and formed the focal point of many observatories in the East. Al Battani (died 928 AD) says that they made it larger and larger so as to increase the accuracy of the measurements. In Abu Mahmud Al Chojendi's observatory in Rei, even as early as 994 AD, they chose a radius of 20 metres for the largest quadrant. It was enclosed in a narrow high room, so that only a thin beam of light fell through a small opening in the ceiling on to the divisions of the circular scale when the sun was in the south.

Al Biruni, a contemporary of Al Chojendi, likewise constructed an enlarged, fixed Ptolemaic quadrant with a radius of approximately 7.5 metres. In his book *Al Quanun al Masudi*,[17] he explained and justified the construction of large stone quadrants on the grounds that metal rings of a similar size were inaccurate because they could easily lose their shape.

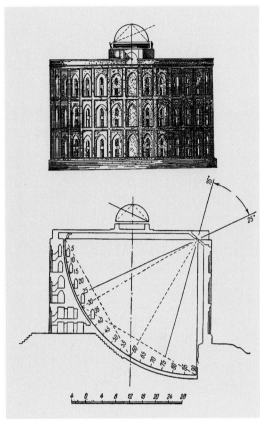

Fig. 23 Reconstruction of the observatory in Samarkand, 15th century: general view (top); vertical section (bottom).

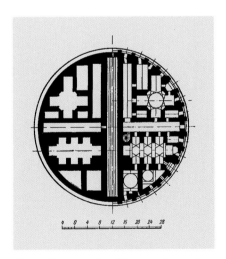

Fig. 22 Reconstruction of the ground plan of the observatory in Samarkand, 15th century, after the latest excavations.

Maragha, 13th century AD

One of the most famous observatories of the East was built in the 13th century AD in Maragha, south of Tabriz. The Mongol ruler Holagu, following the suggestions of the astronomer Nasir al Din al Tusi, had observation instruments built outside the town on a levelled-off mountain ridge. Here, too, they took special care over the stone quadrant. To begin with, the Indian teak quadrant was firmly fixed on the east side of a wall aligned with the meridian. It consisted of a horizontal and a vertical beam and the quarter circle made up of several pieces. They put copper rulers into the straight beam and into the quarter circle a quadrant cast in copper with a measuring scale. A rotating sighting arm with alidades was placed in the centre of the circle.

Samarkand, 1417

Ulugh Beg, grandson of the famous conqueror Timur, planned an observatory for Samarkand on the model of the observatories at Maragha and Rei. Jai Singh refers to Ulugh Beg's work in his writings.

In 1417, Ulugh Beg summoned the best-known Asian astronomers to a conference in his home town. They studied the plans of all the known observatories in existence and then designed a huge building to be situated on a higher site on the Kuchak hill outside the city walls. As its first priority, the building was to include an enormous quadrant.

The precise architectural form of the building had always been unclear right up to the time of the excavations between 1948 and 1951. V. L.

Vjatkin, who had led the first excavations in Samarkand in 1908, merely reconstructed two high walls in alignment with the meridian at both sides of the marble quadrants and a large horizontal circle surrounding the meridian walls (fig. 24).

After the excavations carried out between 1948 and 1951, it emerged that the circular foundations found by Vjatkin had not supported a horizontal circle, but rather the external wall of a building several storeys high. The discovery was consistent with the account provided by the first Great Mogul, Babur, who mentions a three-storied observatory at Samarkand in his travel writings.

The circular observatory (fig. 22) is divided into four quadrants: from north to south by the hall containing the great mural quadrants; and from east to west by corresponding halls of half that length. The workshops, libraries, collections of instruments and work cabinets are accommodated in these four sections of the building. The ground plan elevates the observatory, above what was necessary for its function, into a model of the conception of the world based on the right angle and circle mentioned at the beginning of this chapter and investigated in detail by C. G. Jung.[18] Symmetry and axiality are not being used aesthetically here, but are signs of the astronomical order of the universe for the exploration of which the building was to be used.

The quaternity symbolism of the ground plan is not visible in the façades because there was no formal aesthetic intent. The circular building's purpose was emphasised by its being covered in dark blue and light blue tiles. According to the reports of one of Ulugh Beg's contemporaries, Abd Arasak, the walls of the internal rooms were covered with frescoes on which were portrayed the celestial sphere, the fixed stars and the earth with its mountains and climatic zones.

Those responsible for the design of the astronomical instruments were Chias ad Din Dschemschied and Nizam ad Din al Kashi. Al Kashi came from Fergana where, in 1416, he had already demanded that an observatory should be built. But when he saw no possibility of realizing his plans in Fergana, he went to Samarkand and convinced Ulugh Beg that it was essential to build an especially large observatory for producing accurate horoscopes.

The building was completed in 1420. News about the largest quadrant ever to be constructed first reached the Mediterranean countries and Europe in the middle of the 15th century, when Ali ad Din ibn Muhammad Quschtschi, the last director of the observatory, went to Constantinople to the court of Sultan Mohammed II after Ulugh Beg's death. In 1447, the observations were abandoned in Samarkand and as early as half a century later the observatory stood in ruins.

When Jai Singh was planning his observatories in India at the beginning of the 18th century, even the last traces of the richest observatory in Central Asia were being obscured by desert sand. A detailed description of Ulugh Beg's instruments and astronomical charts survived, however, and gave a real impetus to the astronomical and architectural work of Jai Singh. The maharaja wrote about Beg's building plans in the *Zig Muhammad Shahi*, which was a synthesis of all his work in astronomy.[19]

Although this was such an enormous task that none of the mighty Rajas nor any of the Islamic people had tackled it since the time of the martyr-prince Ulugh Beg – whose sins are forgiven him – nor any of the kings of the past three hundred years who might have possessed the necessary power and dignity … he (Jai Singh) took heart and built here in Delhi several astronomical instruments similar to those which had been constructed in Samarkand.

Let us take another look at Ulugh Beg's quadrant. The great north-south hall takes up all

18 Carl Gustav Jung, *Aion*, in *Collected Works of C. G. Jung*, vol. 9, Princeton University Press, 1969.
19 Written in 1728, it was dedicated to the Mogul Muhammed Shah. English translation.

three storeys of the circular building and extends deep into the roughly hewn cliff beneath it. The ratio of the height of the building (29.21 metres) and the radius of the quadrant (40.20 metres) were chosen so that exactly 45° of the scale lay underground and 45° above ground. Locating

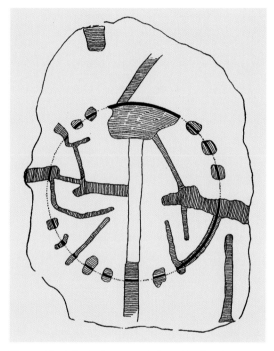

Fig. 24   Ulugh Beg's observatory in Samarkand, 15th century. Plan of site following the first excavations by V. L. Vjatkin.

half of the quadrant underground had several advantages. The main one was that the circular scales made of marble could be mounted directly on to the base of the rock and would therefore be less vulnerable to movement through subsidence – a preventive measure which could also have considerably increased the accuracy of Jai Singh's instruments.

Measurements in Samarkand reveal that those parts of the scales which still exist underground show a deviation of only 3' from north to south, and this small error could have been caused by seismic vibrations. How did they check the

accuracy and the direction of the measuring scales at the time of construction? In Samarkand, as a standard measure for the whole building, it is thought that they laid a strong smooth wooden beam between two thick brick walls in a precise north-south orientation prior to construction. In Jaipur, the astronomers established the north-south axis on a broad stone platform (called 'Jai Singh's Seat') into which a large horizontal circle was set (fig. 86).

Fragments of a horizontal stone circle have also been found in Samarkand. These, however, presumably belong to a relatively small instrument on the roof of the observatory with which they could measure azimuthal and altitudinal angles, the so-called azimuthal quadrant.

Instruments of the same kind were used in many Arabian observatories and also on Uraniborg, Tycho Brahe's castle and observatory. These usually consisted of an upright azimuthal quadrant which could be rotated on its perpendicular axis. A sighting arm in the plane of the quadrant was used for measuring altitudinal angles; the horizontal lower edge of the quadrant was situated above a horizontal circle.

Jai Singh was naturally acquainted with these and other similar instruments. A variant, essentially consisting of a drum-shaped body whose lower end is closed by a circular disc, was the model for his Rama Yantras (figs. 40, 41, 74, 94–96, 146) and Digamsa Yantras (figs. 42, 43).

In his writings, Jai Singh refers exclusively to Greek and Arab astronomers. This therefore suggests we should seek the models for his buildings primarily in the Middle East, where they had been constantly improving and enlarging small, ancient measuring instruments. However, some particularly large Central European instruments evolved into buildings similar to those of Jai Singh. Since there had always been European Jesuits at the maharaja's court who were familiar with the instruments of European astronomers, it is likely that Jai Singh also came to hear about one or other of these instruments.

Uraniborg, c. 1580

Fig. 25 Site plan of Uraniborg, the observatory built by Danish astronomer Tycho Brahe on the island of Ven, c. 1580.

Around 150 years before Jai Singh, a European prince and astronomer, Tycho Brahe (1546–1601), had also hoped for better results from very large instruments. He had built a magnificent observatory, Uraniborg, which in many respects could be compared to those of Jai Singh.

During his law studies, the young nobleman had discovered a new star while conducting secret work on astronomy and this discovery was used as an opportunity to write a book, *De nova stella*, mainly devoted to astrology.[20] Like most of his contemporaries, he had no doubt about the viability of astrological calculations and predictions. A sharp division between astronomy, mathematics, geometry and astrology seemed neither necessary nor desirable at that time. It was easy to find a causal link between the formation of the universe and earthly events. Therefore, it is not surprising that the lectures which Tycho Brahe gave at the University of Copenhagen on the request of the Danish king Frederick II were primarily about astrology, although the subject of the lectures was 'De disciplinis mathematicis'.

On the recommendation of the Landgrave William IV of Hesse, Frederick II offered to support Tycho Brahe in his astronomical research, giving him the uninhabited island of Ven, near Copenhagen, for life as a place to build a new observatory. The island was perfectly suited to astronomical observation since from its highest point you could see the horizon in all directions.

The architects Jan van Paschen and Jan van Stenwinkel were successively commissioned to plan and execute a building which was to serve simultaneously as a castle and an observatory. On Tycho Brahe's advice, they constructed a building the central part of which was square (fig. 27). It was situated diagonally in the centre of a park which was also laid out in a square (fig. 25).

Fig. 26 Tycho Brahe's azimuthal quadrant was constructed in the same way as the reconstructed azimuthal quadrant on the roof of the observatory in Samarkand, c. 1580.

The corners of the grounds, which are surrounded by walls, face the four main compass points. Wide paths lead from the entrance gates in the east and west corners to a circular area in the centre; at right angles to them, running through the park diagonally again, are two further paths leading to the buildings in the south and north corners, the printing room and the servants' quarters.

What is remarkable about this plan is the double symmetry and the exclusive use of geometrical shapes, namely the square and the circle. Tycho Brahe, who describes Uraniborg in his *Astronomiae instauratae mechanica*, makes no mention of the reasons for the strict layout and

20 Copenhagen, 1573.

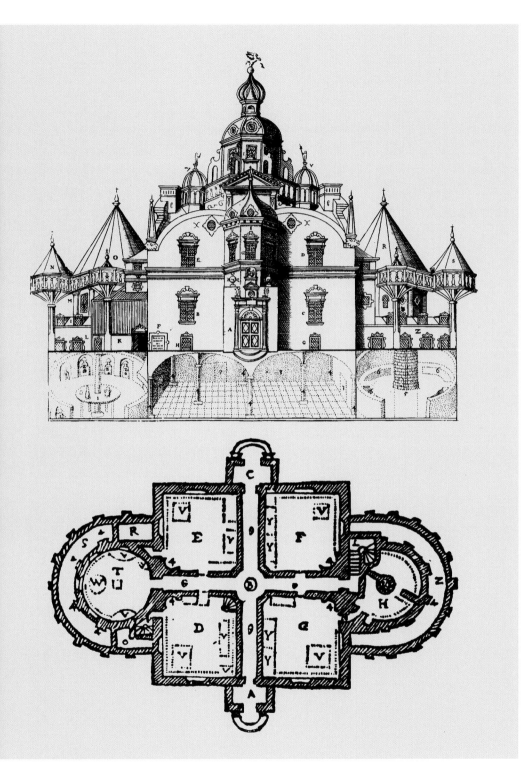

Fig. 27 The castle and observatory built by Tycho Brahe, c. 1580. The layout is imbued with geometrical and astronomical symbolism.

21 Tycho Brahe, *Astronomiae instauratae mechanica*, 1598.

the orientation towards the four compass points. But if we consider the significance of cosmological speculation and astrology in Tycho Brahe's life then we might recognise in the layout more than just a fashion of the time – a quaternity symbol *par excellence*.

The castle itself was also laid out exclusively according to geometrical and astronomical considerations, to the extent that obvious functional shortcomings were accepted. The façades of the square section of the building face the four compass points. Four long halls in the axes divide the ground plan into four square living rooms and bedrooms. At the point where the halls intersect, there is a round fountain with a statue spurting out water. The entrances lie on the east-west axis; on the north-south axis, circular buildings adjoin the central square section. The library was in the circular building to the south, the kitchen to the north. Above them were the real observation rooms, on an octagonal ground plan and protected by light, conical roofs which could be opened and shut as desired. Under the kitchen and library were the store-rooms and chemical laboratory.

Tycho Brahe himself gives us the following information about the layout (fig. 27):

(A) the east entrance, executed in the Doric and Ionic style, (B) the winter dining-room, (C) an additional bedroom; two more are on the west side, (M) studio and library, (L) the underground circular laboratory with sixteen different melting furnaces, (N) the small south observatory, (O) the large south observatory, (E) the blue room; a large green summer dining-room facing west, (D) the red room, (R) the large north observatory, (S) the small north observatory.[21]

In its geometrical design, Uraniborg is reminiscent of Ulugh Beg's observatory in Samarkand. Here, too, the ground plan was built on a main axis lying in the meridian plane, the halls divide

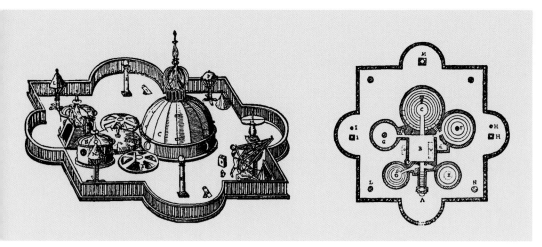

Fig. 28   In 1584, Tycho Brahe built a second, smaller observatory near Uraniborg called Stjerneborg.

Fig. 29   The large equatorial armillary sphere in Stjerneborg, 1584.

22 Ibid.
23 Johann A. Repsold, *Zur Geschichte der astronomischen Meßwerkzeuge 1450–1830*, Leipzig, 1908.

the building into four quadrants, and the architect's designs were based on the circle and the square.

In Jai Singh's observatories, symbolic characteristics of this nature are not so easy to detect. The reasons for this will be investigated in chapter 3.

Stjerneborg, 1548

Construction of Uraniborg was completed in 1580 and, within a few years, the lonely 'castle of the sky' blossomed into a magnificent prince's palace. Tycho Brahe, however, dissatisfied with the accuracy of his assistants' measurements at Uraniborg and driven by an obsessive compulsion to build newer and larger instruments, started to tackle a new building project:

Since, for certain reasons, I had had far more instruments made than I could accommodate without one being in the way of the other when in use, later, around 1584, I built, with no inconsiderable difficulty, on a hill outside the castle at a distance of around 70 feet from the wall, an underground

observatory, which had several cellars, all made in heavy brick ... I called this observatory Stjerneborg.[22]

Naturally, the plan of Stjerneborg was also derived from basic geometrical shapes (fig. 28). For the perimeter of the site, Tycho Brahe chose a square with semicircular bays in the middle of each side, in other words the same shape as the perimeter wall of Uraniborg, only this time it is not the diagonals which are oriented towards the compass points but the axes of the square. He again chose the meridian line as the axis of symmetry.

The observatory is entered from the north on this line. A staircase leads down into the square underground living room, around which there are five circular observation rooms. The largest one to the south contains an enormous equatorial armillary sphere (diameter 2.72 metres).

Generally there was an emerging trend towards large dimensions, and with good reason because, though it occasionally hindered construction, viewing through alidades demands these dimensions in order to obtain greater accuracy ... On the other hand, it was probably a mistake if the workshops were laid out and maintained on too large a scale. One has the impression that the instruments were built purely to create work, similar to Tycho's poems which he dedicated to good friends, and which he had printed in order to make work for his papermill.[23]

These words by J. A. Repsold could well be applied to Jai Singh. But this man designed instruments ten times larger than Tycho Brahe and built not two observatories but five.

In his *Astronomiae instauratae mechanica*, Tycho Brahe left us with an accurate description of all his instruments and buildings. But when he turned his back on Denmark in 1588, following

Fig. 30 Tycho Brahe's mural quadrant, 1584.

numerous arguments with Frederick II's successor, the observatories quickly fell into disrepair. He went to Prague, but did not build a new observatory there, as Emperor Rudolph was not able to make a suitable castle available to him with an uninterrupted view of the horizon.

We have already seen that the largest and most important instrument in Ulugh Beg's observatory was the marble quadrant. Jai Singh copied it in Jaipur and Delhi as a Shastansha Yantra. Even in Tycho Brahe's description, the mural quadrant is explicitly mentioned as being the most important instrument (fig. 30).

Fig. 31 The 13th-century observatory in Peking, as it was in the 17th century with the Jesuits' instruments.

Peking, 13th–17th century

Chinese astronomers were already using the armillary sphere with equatorial and meridian circles around 100 BC and large brass quadrants from around AD 600.

The devices preserved in the Peking observatory today were only installed at the end of the 17th century and were based on Tycho Brahe's instruments. Verbiest, a Jesuit, had conducted an experiment in 1673 to demonstrate to the emperor and the mandarins of the astronomy department that the brass instruments which had been in use there since the 13th century were flawed. His predecessor, the Jesuit Schall, had already documented the superiority of European instruments and European astronomy in Peking. However, as in Indian observatories, telescopes were not used until the 18th century.

a) staircase
b) living accommodation
c) armillary sphere
d) celestial sphere
e) zodiacal armillary
f) azimuth instrument
g) quadrant
h) sextant
i) observation tower with
   warmth hole for astronomers

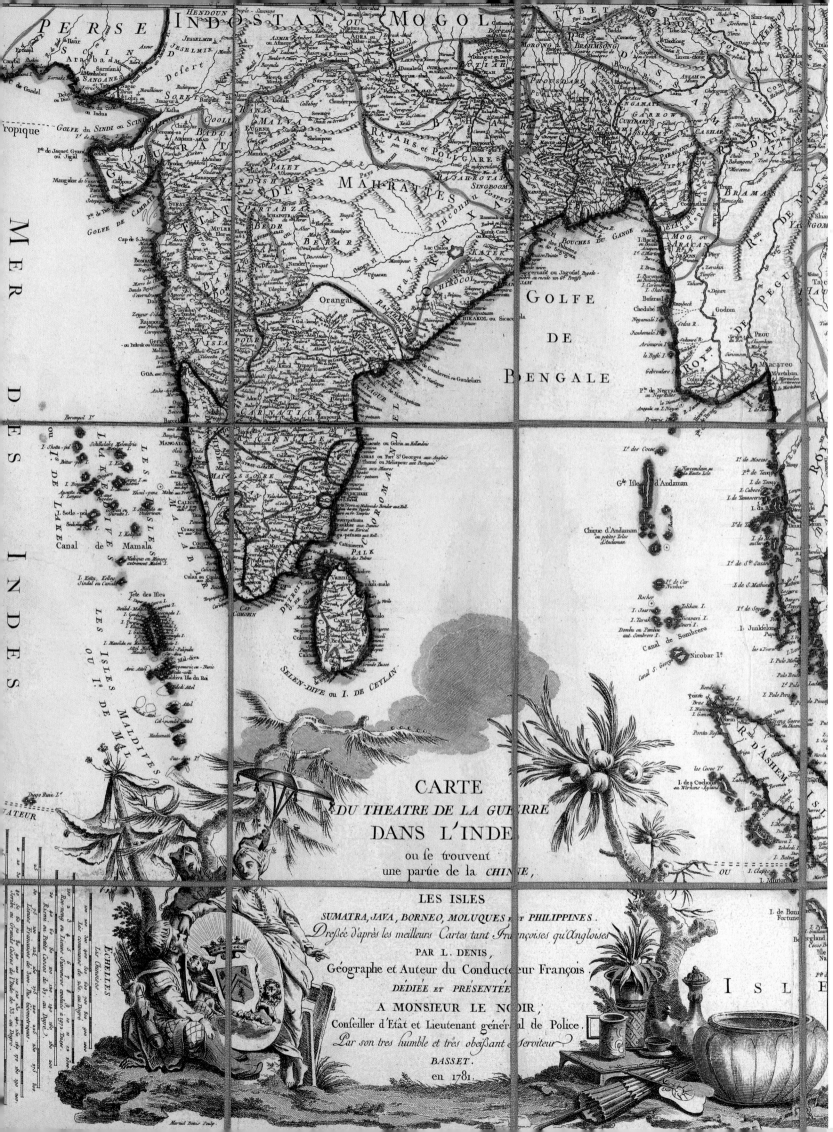

2 | Maharaja Jai Singh II and his Observatories

*Fig. 32   Maharaja Sawai Jai Singh II of Jaipur
(1686–1743).*

*Fig. 33   Traders and missionaries ensured
an ongoing scientific exchange between Europe
and India.*

Even during the lifetime of the most famous of all the Great Moguls of India, Shah Jahan, his two sons engaged in a fierce battle for the succession to the throne. The victor, Aurangzeb, became the sixth Great Mogul of India, expanding the kingdom into an empire which stretched from Kabul to Madras. The new shah's fanatical devotion to Islam, however, deepened the rift between Hindus and Muslims and led to the decline of the Mogul dynasty. Cultural life at the Delhi court began to wane. The dancers, singers, painters and architects moved to the courts of the provincial governors and to the Hindu maharajas. One of the Hindu princes who came into the cultural inheritance of the Moguls was Jai Singh II of Amber (later Maharaja of Jaipur), who inherited the principality when he was thirteen.

Jai Singh was twenty when Aurangzeb died. In the battle over the succession, he sided with the opponents of Alum Bahadur. The latter won the war, however, and occupied the principality of Amber. Jai Singh only succeeded in winning back his castle by a sudden lightning attack, during which he finally managed to drive out the imperial troops.

In spite of this and similar acts of defiance against the ruling family in Delhi, Jai Singh acknowledged in principle the hegemony of the Moguls and fought on their side right up until the reign of the Mogul Muhammad Shah (1719–1748). In recognition of this loyalty, Muhammad Shah named him governor of the provinces of Agra and Malwa. For his part, Jai Singh strengthened their friendship by dedicating his astronomical tables to the emperor in 1728.

Not until the Persian emperor Nadir Shah invaded India in 1739 did Jai Singh, like most of the Hindu princes, abandon the Mogul. Supporting him was useless, since Muhammad Shah only had a few bodyguards to oppose the Persian army outside the gates of Delhi.

Jai Singh made use of the short spells of time between individual campaigns to devote himself to those activities for which he is ultimately remembered: astronomy and architecture. His greatest building project was the foundation of a new royal capital. During the first years of his rule, he had developed the old family seat, Amber Castle, into a magnificent Mogul-style edifice. But he finally abandoned this stronghold situated in a strategically favourable position, since the surrounding mountains prevented any further extension to the grounds and, furthermore, contaminated water from the well had often led to bouts of sickness. The new town was founded in 1728 and was given the name Jaipur, which means 'the town of victory' (for town plan, see fig. 99). Since this time, the princes of Amber have been known as 'Maharaja of Jaipur'.

Jaipur is one of the few towns in India which was built on a rectilinear street plan. Although all the well-known Hindu architectural manuals favour such a plan, no settlements before or after display such a clear geometrical layout. Admittedly there are some pre-Aryan towns known from the Indus Valley culture dating back to early history (2500–1500 BC), such as Mohenjo Daro and Harappa, which have an almost rectangular street plan. Given the 3,700-year time gap, however, there can hardly be any direct link between this pre-Aryan urbanism and that of Jaipur. Nevertheless, there are some amazing parallels. In both instances, a primary communication network of broad streets for the palanquins and carriages runs through the multistoried residential buildings at regular intervals, and in both towns the large blocks are surrounded by a secondary network of narrow footpaths.

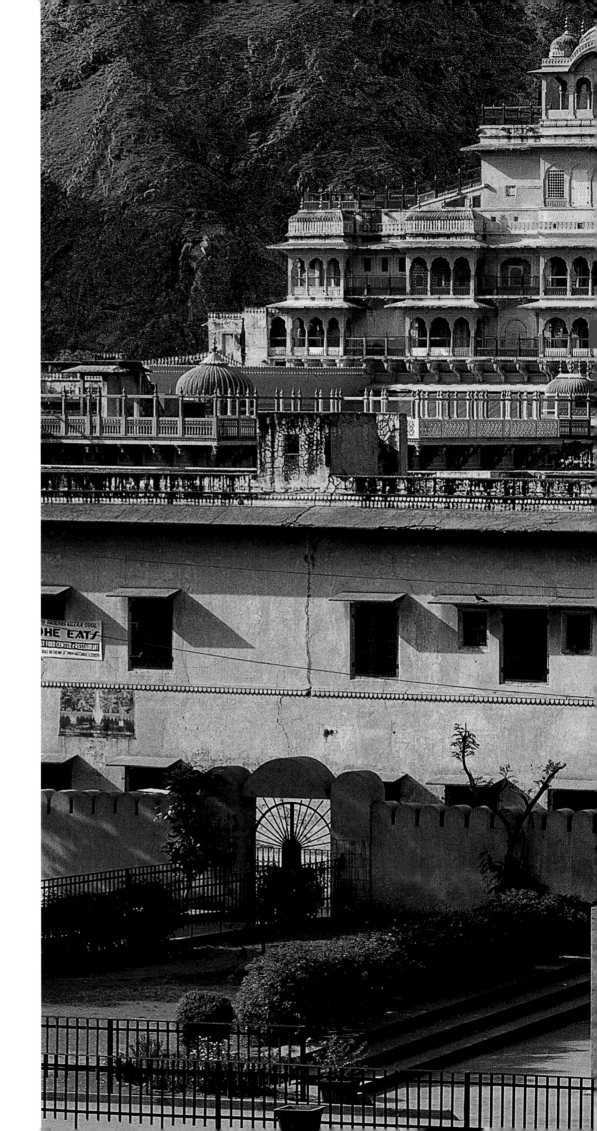

Fig. 34 The maharaja's palace in Jaipur, with the observatory in the foreground.

Page 34
Fig. 35 The numerous courtyards of the palace in Jaipur contain magnificent halls in the Mogul style, bearing witness to the power and wealth of Maharaja Jai Singh II.

Page 35
Fig. 36 At the entrance to his private quarters, the present maharaja, Bhawani Singh (left), and one of his attendants (right) are expecting guests.

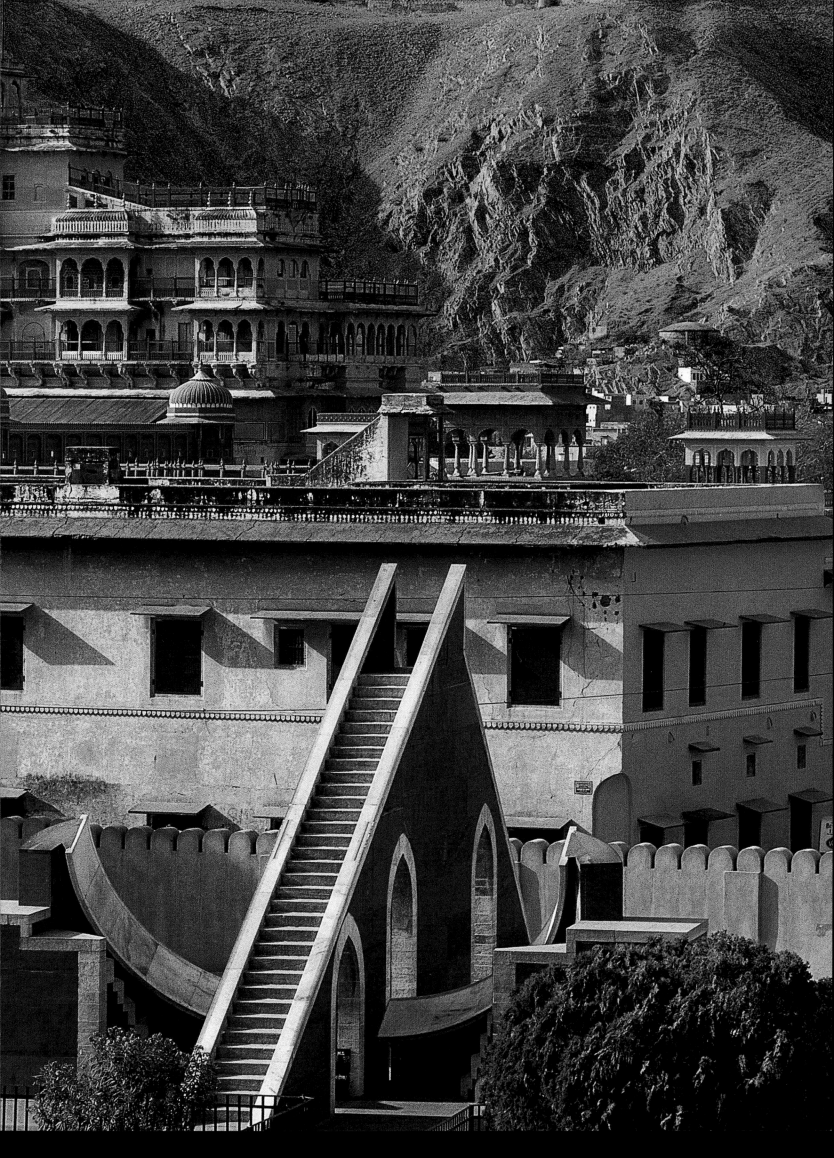

There is another innovation in Jaipur reminiscent of Mohenjo Daro and Harappa: a stream ran underground into the town enabling public wells to be built at regular intervals. This improvement in the sanitation, subsequently copied in other Indian towns, was matched by a project which was equally far-sighted. Running along the middle of the street was a sewer covered with large stone slabs to which almost all the houses were connected.

In the centre of the town of Jaipur is the palace. It differs from earlier Mogul palaces in that the central part on several floors is pyramid-shaped. This type of structure is found in its purest form in the Hindu palace of Datiya in Bundelkhand[24] and the Kotilal[25] in Delhi. The Moguls rejected the traditional and highly symbolic Indian multi-storied pyramid in favour of spaced-out rows of single-storied columned halls with gardens and expanses of water. Such differences between the Mogul buildings and those of the Hindu princes demonstrate that the latter did not automatically adopt the building styles of the Islamic imperial houses everywhere – a significant factor in the analysis of the form and construction of Jai Singh's instruments.

2.1 THE OBSERVATORY IN THE PALACE OF JAIPUR

The orientation of the streets of Jaipur deviates considerably from the four compass points (fig. 99). All the houses, as well as the palace itself, take their orientation from that of the streets. The observatory, whose instruments are laid out according to their astronomical function, is situated in one of the courtyards of the palace.

Fig. 37 View of the observatory from the palace wall.

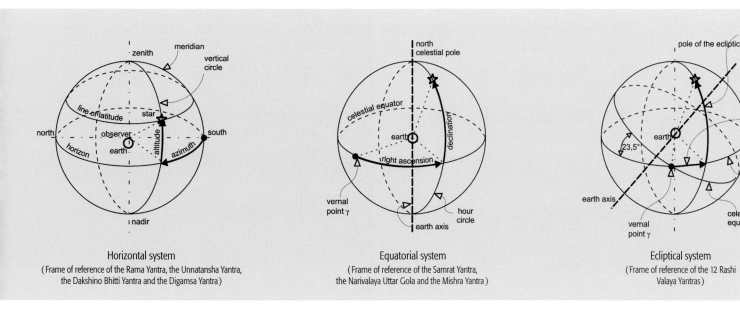

*Fig. 38 Alternative coordination systems
for astronomical measurement.*

The difference in orientation between the walls of the courtyard and the instruments is particularly noticeable where large instruments stand next to the courtyard's perimeter wall (fig. 86). This characteristic could only have been avoided if they had made two perimeter walls, each one facing a different direction. A few years earlier, a similar problem had been solved when the so-called Pearl Mosque in the Red Fort of Delhi was built. Here the Quibla, the direction of Mecca accepted as being precisely west, had to be adhered to; but the Red Fort, like the palace of Jaipur, deviated from this by a few degrees.[26]

One of the earliest descriptions we have of the observatory in the palace of Jaipur is by Father Joseph Tieffenthaler. It is reproduced here in full as it dates from the year 1754, or possibly even from 1747, before any restorations or additions had taken place.

But above all, the place which deserves some comment and which was built for astronomical observations is a building such has never been seen in this country before, and which, on account of its novelty as well as its large number of instruments,

is therefore worthy of our admiration. It is situated near the castle on an open plain; it is large and spacious, surrounded by walls and equipped for observing the sky.

First of all, at the entrance we see the twelve signs of the zodiac, each of which is divided up by large circles made of pure limestone. In addition, there are all kinds of cross-sections of astronomical spheres averaging one or more feet in diameter built according to the local polar altitude; then, large and small equinoctial sundials and astrolabes, also made of limestone; and finally, the meridian line and a horizontal sundial carved into a very large stone.

Quite outstanding, however, is a representation of an extremely tall axis of the celestial sphere, made of bricks and limestone, in the meridian plane and built at an angle equal to the local latitude; it could be 70 Parisian feet high. High up on this axis is the vantage point from which you can look down over the town, but not without feeling dizzy. The shadow of this huge axis falls on an enormously large astronomical quadrant (semicircle), whose projections and curved

24 See *Living Achitecture: Islamic Indian*
    by the author, p. 141.
25 Ibid. p. 141.
26 Ibid. p. 48.

ends point upwards; it is divided into degrees and minutes; a very skilful piece of work fashioned in the whitest limestone or plaster. In the morning, the shadow falls on the quadrant on the west side and in the afternoon it falls on the other side on the east, in such a way that the axis of the celestial sphere remains in the middle between the two quadrants and the height of the sun can be found at any moment.

Alongside these gnomons, there is a double quadrant, also made of plaster; it is enclosed in a room in which one rises up on each side. At noon, the sun's rays fall through two holes in a copper disc and show noon altitude on each quadrant, below the centre in summer and above it in winter.

Not least remarkable are the three large astrolabes hanging on movable iron rings alongside a brass ring with a sighting arm and rings built towards the polar altitude to establish the declination of the sun, which it is possible to see at any time so long as the instrument is directed at the sun. I shall ignore any smaller instruments.

Amongst the imperfections of this observatory, however, are not only its low-lying situation and the walls around it, which make it impossible to observe the rising and setting of the stars, but also the fact that the gnomon, the axis of the celestial sphere, and other instruments are made of plaster, making it impossible to obtain very accurate readings.[27]

Even though this description is not clear on all points, it nevertheless still proves that a series of instruments which, right up until modern times,

were ascribed to Jai Singh's successors must have already existed in his lifetime. This applies above all to the twelve small so-called Rashi Valaya Yantras (fig. 58), which Tieffenthaler mentions at the beginning.

Among the instruments which Jai Singh built in Jaipur, Delhi, Benares, Ujjain and Mathura, we come across the same types of measuring devices again and again. In the observatory at Jaipur, which is the largest, all the different types are represented. It is therefore useful to explain the way the instruments work on the basis of the examples built in Jaipur. The buildings can be divided into four categories:

a) instruments which enable measurements relating to the horizon and the zenith to be taken, for example the Rama Yantra (figs. 40, 41, 94, 95, 96) and Digamsa Yantra (figs. 42, 43),

b) instruments, which enable measurements relating to the equator and the earth's axis to be taken, for example the Samrat Yantra (figs. 44, 46, 47, 87, 88),

c) instruments which allow measurements to be taken actually in the ecliptical system, for example the Rashi Valaya Yantras (figs. 58, 59, 89, 90),

d) buildings not used directly for measuring purposes, for example 'Jai Singh's Seat' and the 'Astronomer's House' (site plan see fig. 86).

27 Translated from the German translation of Joseph Tieffenthaler's work by J. Bernoulli, *Beschreibung von Hindustan*, Berlin, 1785, pp. 224f.

Fig. 39 Reception building in the maharaja's palace in Jaipur.

The Rama Yantra

For measuring the azimuth and zenith distances (or the altitude) of a star, a circular horizontal surface with a graduated scale radiating from the centre was used and a vertical post was placed in the centre. The azimuth of the sun could then be read directly by the shadow cast by the stick on the circular scale; stars have to be observed from the plane by using the tip of the stick. To make this possible, they cut sectors of 12° or 18° out of the circular surface – rather like cutting out every other piece from a round flan. The sectors of the circle that were removed were assembled into a second similarly incomplete measuring scale, so that the two scales made up a whole (fig. 40). All the sectors were made of stone and constructed on high ground. The observer could walk into the spaces and cast his eye along the edges of the stone sectors and observe a star from there. Presumably in order to make observations easier, they used a thread which was attached to the tip of the gnomon and could be moved backwards and forwards as a sighting line along the edges.

For determining the zenith distance, they inscribed concentric circles on to the circular surface whose intervals were provided by the projection of a vertical scale on the quadrant (a so-called tangential scale). In order to avoid touching intersections while observing stars with a very large zenith distance and in order also to avoid having scales that were impossibly long, they chose the radius of the circular surface to be the same length as the gnomon. Thus zenith distances up to a maximum of 45° could be measured. They projected the remaining 45° of the aforementioned quadrant – again as a tangential scale – on to a circular wall which surrounds the surface of the circle and is the same height as the gnomon. They also cut strips out of this wall, each 12° or 18° wide (fig. 41).

To test this new type of instrument out, Jai Singh first of all built two small Rama Yantras in Jaipur which together form a whole, each with a radius of 0.865 metres (fig. 94), and then the large Rama Yantras four times the size (figs. 95, 96) with a diameter of 3.442 metres. Drum-shaped sundials of a similar kind had been in use for centuries in both the East and the West, but the division of the body of the drum into two complementary instruments and the monumental execution can be attributed to Jai Singh.

The inventor certainly already considered it a disadvantage of this new building that it was only possible to observe stars with the accuracy he desired when they had moved by a full 12° or 18°. Moreover, the graduations carved radially into the sectors of the circle could only be used for determining the azimuth of the sun with the aid of the gnomon. This shortcoming led Jai Singh's astronomers to build a variant of the Rama Yantra, a Digamsa Yantra.

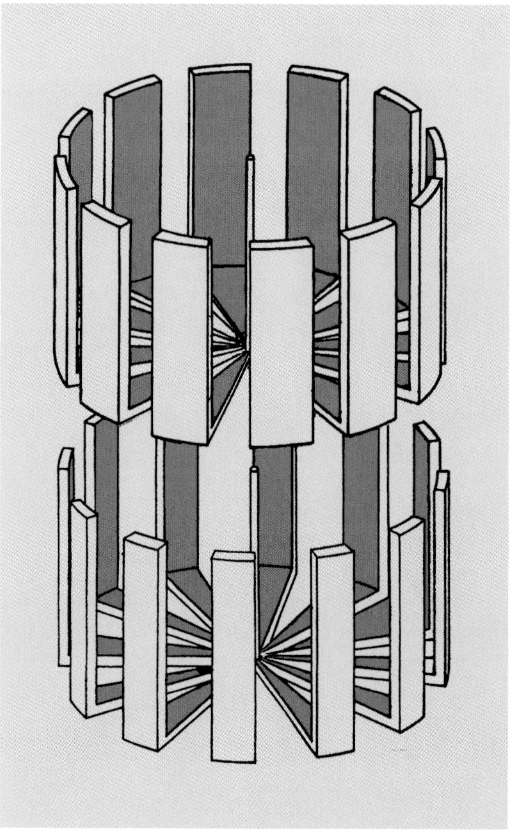

Fig. 40 The Rama Yantra, whose two instruments make up a whole.

Fig. 41   The western Great Rama Yantra (drum sundial), Jaipur. The stone sector-shaped graduated areas of each of the two Rama Yantras together make a complete circle.

The Digamsa Yantra

The Digamsa Yantra's only purpose was to determine azimuthal angles, something it was able do with greater accuracy than the Rama Yantra. Hunter quotes a description of its construction and the way it worked from the *Samrat Siddhanta*, one of the books (subsequently lost) which were written in Jai Singh's observatory during his lifetime:[28]

> On a horizontal plane describe the three concentric circles A, B, C, and draw the north, south, east, and west lines, as in the figure. Then on A build a solid pillar, of any height at pleasure; on B build a wall, equal in height to the pillar at A; and on C a wall of double that height. From the north, south, east, and west points, on the top of the wall C stretch the threads N. S. W. E. intersecting each other in the point D, directly above the centre of the pillar A. To the centre of that pillar, fasten a thread, which is to be laid over the top of the wall C, and to be stretched by a weight suspended to the other end of it.

The observer now went to stand between walls B and C, whilst his assistant moved the string backwards and forwards along a graduated scale on the upper edge of wall C until the star, the point of intersection of the cross hairs and the sighting string were all aligned for the observer. The assistant could now read the azimuthal angle accurately on the graduated scale.

The construction of the Rama Yantras and Digamsa Yantras did not make too great a demand on the Maharaja's architects. They could produce circles, perpendicular walls and horizontal planes with the aid of simple instruments and easily check their accuracy afterwards.

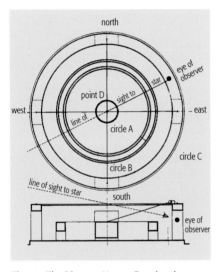

Fig. 42 The Digamsa Yantra. Functional diagram after Jai Singh.

28 William Hunter, 'Some Accounts of the Astronomical Labours of Jayasinha', in *Asiatic Researches*, vol. 5, 1799, pp. 197–98.

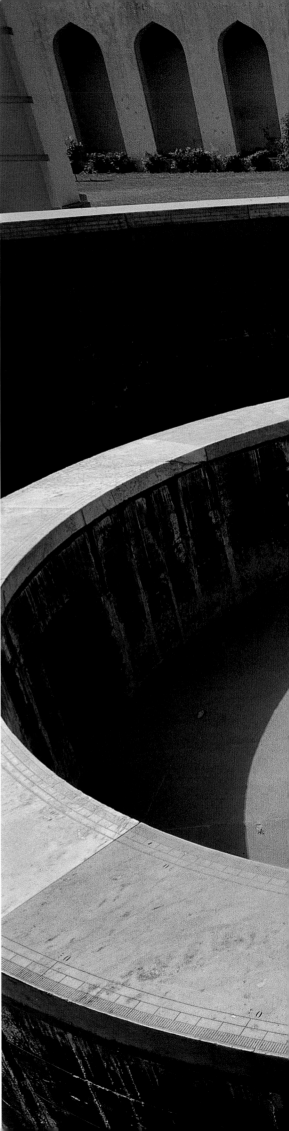

Fig. 43 The Digamsa Yantra, Jaipur, makes it possible to measure the azimuth of the sun or of a star.

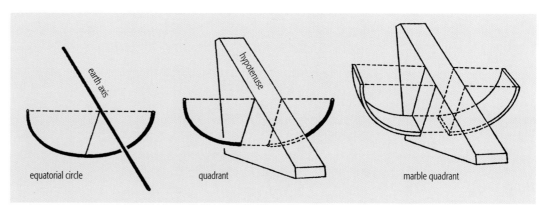

equatorial circle   quadrant   marble quadrant

Fig. 45   The development of a Samrat Yantra.

Fig. 44   The Great Samrat Yantra, Jaipur. This so-called 'royal instrument' is by far the largest and most lavish of Jai Singh's buildings. Although constructed on a sunken square platform, it still towers above the rooftops of the town. View from the north-east towards the west tower, which supports one of the two quadrants of the equatorial circle. Inside the tower there is – as in the model of the observatory at Samarkand – a meridian quadrant (Shastansha Yantra) with a diameter of over 16 metres.

The Samrat Yantra

The construction of the largest of all the instruments, the Samrat Yantra, placed much greater demands on the skill of the architects and astronomers. There were even models of this building. Sibt al Maridini (1423–1495) from Damascus and the 16th-century German astronomers Sebastian Münster (1489–1552) and Johann Schroner[29] were the first people to use sundials with a gnomon, called a pole stick or polos, which pointed to the celestial pole.

In this case, too, Jai Singh's contribution probably lay in the enlargement and improvement of details. The building of the polos, and eventually the Samrat Yantra, was motivated by the following question: why should we always only measure the position of the stars in relation to the horizon, since the horizon is inevitably different for observatories in other towns? Why not design all the instruments the same so that the readings relate directly to the equator and the earth's axis? This would make it unnecessary to convert the different azimuthal and altitudinal angles into this more sensible reference frame, and readings from different observatories could be directly

29 According to E. Zinner, *Deutsche und niederländische astronomische Instrumente,* Munich, 1967.

Fig. 47   The Great Samrat Yantra, Jaipur. A system of water channels on the ground forms the reference level for all the instruments.

Fig. 46   The Great Samrat Yantra, Jaipur. The steps up
both sides of the marble equatorial circle lead in a wide
curve to the west tower. Every point of the measuring
scale (diameter 30.36 metres) is accessible via these steps.

compared with each other. The only difficulty was that instruments of this kind were not as simple to build and adjust as a Rama Yantra or a Digamsa Yantra.

In principle, the Samrat Yantra simply consists of (1) a straight line lying in the meridian plane and pointing to the celestial pole (in other words a line parallel to the earth's axis), and (2) a semicircle which is standing vertically on this straight line, thereby forming a plane parallel to the equator (fig. 45).

The artificial earth's axis and the artificial equator fully fulfil their function as frames of reference for the astronomical reading of angles, even though they are not installed in the centre of the earth but on its surface, because the earth's diameter can be disregarded in astronomical orders of magnitude. If we observe a star from the arc just above the straight line – there is only ever one possibility for that – then we can read the right ascension on the circle and the declination on the straight line (providing of course that a scale of degrees is put on the arc and a tangential scale on the straight line).

The straight line and the arc, these are the simple shapes Jai Singh started out with when developing his fantastic three-dimensional constructions. It was of prime importance to build a wall in the meridian plane, whose upper edge pointed to the celestial pole. The geographical latitude of the place determined the angle between this straight line and the horizontal plane. The wall was sensibly given the shape of a right-angled triangle. The edge pointing to the pole is its hypotenuse. The thickness of the meridian wall meant that instead of one hypotenuse there were two at the edges of the wall. Therefore, in place of a semicircular equator they now also had to make two separate quarter circles or quadrants in the equatorial plane. But these quadrants could also not be made as razor-sharp, two-dimensional lines, so they replaced them with wide strips of marble which had a graduated scale on both sides.

When observing stars south of the equator, they looked from the north across the northern edge of the quadrants and the corresponding hypotenuse. When observing stars north of the equator, they used the graduation on the southern edge of the quadrants since now they had to observe the star from the south by the appropriate hypotenuse. This not only resulted in two hypotenuses, but in a total of four separate graduated scales pointing to the south and north on the upper edge of the wall.

The measuring procedure was as follows: the observer ran his eye along the edge of a quadrant until the star was still just visible on the hypotenuse. Then he directed his assistant to take a peg along the hypotenuse until the viewing position of the observer, the tip of the peg on the hypotenuse and the star were all lined up. The assistant now read the declination and the observer the right ascension.

The declination of the sun was determined using the same procedure. They could obtain the right ascension of the sun directly from the position of the shadow which the hypotenuse casts on one of the quadrants. The shadow also gives the time of day (local time). In the morning, when the sun rises in the east, the shadow moves down on the western quadrant by 15° an hour. If the meridian wall does not cast a shadow on one of the quadrants then it is noon. In the afternoon, the shadow moves upwards again on the eastern quadrant.[30]

The Shastansha Yantra

Jai Singh built two mural quadrants like those which had formed the heart of Ulugh Beg's observatory in Samarkand.[31] They were built to a smaller scale in the towers which flank the Great Samrat Yantra to the east and west. In both these towers there is a high, narrow, dark hall running

30 The so-called Small Samrat Yantra stands near the present-day entrance to the observatory. Although it is similar in form and the way it functions to the Great Samrat Yantra, it was built not by Jai Singh, but by the Maharaja Ram Singh in 1876.
31 See p. 23 and fig. 23.

from north to south. The quadrants or sextants, which have a radius of 8.66 metres (in Samarkand 40.20 metres),[32] run along the long walls in the meridian plane. At the centre point of the arcs are the pin-sized holes in copper plates described by Tieffenthaler[33] which allow a thin ray of light through the ceiling of the hall. In the morning the ray of light moves downwards on the west wall of the hall and in the afternoon upwards again on the east wall. At noon precisely, the image of the sun projected by the hole gnomon as a small bright disc appears on the marble quadrants and accurately records the zenith distance of the sun in its meridian transit.

When A. Garrett restored the Jaipur observatory between 1901 and 1902 he found no perforated copper plates in the Shastansha Yantra, only the openings in the wall measuring approximately 10 × 10 centimetres into which these plates were set. His presumption that Jai Singh might nevertheless have used the instrument in one way or another without the hole gnomon shows that he was not familiar with Tieffenthaler's account, which expressly mentions the plates.

Not only was the Shastansha Yantra smaller than Ulugh Beg's quadrant at Samarkand, it was also not as versatile. The hole gnomon only projected the image of the sun or the full moon. It would only have been possible to establish the zenith distance of other stars if they had removed the perforated plates and installed a movable system of alidades on the quadrants. It was precisely this observational equipment which made Ulugh Beg's quadrant so remarkable. The alidades in Samarkand were conveyed in small carriages along channels that were cut into the quadrant's marble. Observational aids such as this are lacking in the Shastansha Yantra. It had neither steps along the quadrant nor channels for movable alidades and, in addition, Tieffenthaler only mentions a hole gnomon. The effort involved in the construction of the building was thus out of all proportion to the instrument's usefulness.

The Dakshino Bhitti Yantra

On the long axis of the Great Samrat Yantra to the north is a plain, two-storey building which is oriented longitudinally precisely north-south. A marble semicircle with a graduated scale is set into its western outer wall. A metal spike in the centre of the arc casts its shadow at the meridian transit of the sun on to the scale engraved in the marble and thus records the daily noon altitude of the sun (fig. 97).

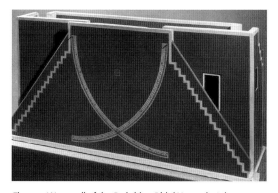

Fig. 48   West wall of the Dakshino Bhitti Yantra in Jaipur. Model made for the Science Museum, London, in 1893.

Here, as in the Shastansha Yantra, it was therefore possible to establish the days of the solstice and calculate the angle between the plane of the ecliptic and that of the earth's equator. However, these figures could be more accurately obtained from the Shastansha Yantra's quadrant. The task of the Dakshino Bhitti Yantra, therefore, was presumably to compensate for the shortcomings of the Shastansha Yantra in observing the stars. By fixing a string to the spike in the middle, it was not difficult to observe a star from the circular scale and obtain the zenith distance from the position of the sighting string.

However, readings were not nearly as accurate as they would have been with the help of the alidades which Ulugh Beg or Tycho Brahe had used.

32 According to N. Leonov, *Naucnyj podrig samarkandskich astronomov*, XV, Moscow, 1960.
33 Joseph Tieffenthaler, *Beschreibung von Hindustan*, translated into German by J. Bernoulli, Berlin, 1785.

The shadow of the metal spike in the afternoon falls as a broad line without a sharply defined edge on to the circular scale subdivided into units of 2'. When observing a star, the thickness of the spike makes it difficult to make full use of the fine gradations. A sighting arm attached to the spike would have considerably improved the accuracy of the readings. But since neither Jai Singh in the *Zig Muhammad Shahi* or Jagannath in the *Samrat Siddhanta,* nor any of the European visitors or restorers, make any mention of alidades this detail remains a puzzle.

On the west side, steps lead on to the roof of the Dakshino Bhitti Yantra. For the convenience of the observer, these steps roughly follow the course of the marble circle. On the east-facing outer wall, that is opposite, are two quadrants which are similarly subdivided into units of 2'. But since there are no corresponding steps here, they do not seem to be suitable for observation purposes.

The rooms on both floors of the building are provided with the usual contemporary profiles. The edges of the profiles are painted white, the wall surfaces red. Under the rubble on the ground floor several models of the measuring instruments came to light during clearance work by the author in 1969. They are compared with the buildings themselves in chapter 4.

The Narivalaya Uttar Gola Yantra

The instruments of this relatively small building consist of two circular surfaces built in red sandstone and white marble (fig. 92). Like the quadrants of the Samrat Yantra, these are inclined so far towards the horizontal plane that they lie parallel to the equatorial plane. A metal spike in the centre which casts a shadow and a division of the disc into degrees and minutes completes the equatorial sundial.

One of the two round surfaces points to the north celestial pole; it can only be used as a sundial in the summer months. During the winter months, the sun shines from the south onto the equatorial plane. For that reason, they built a second circular disc facing south on the south side (fig. 49). An inscription in the centre of this disc, 'Donated by Judge Brahma Deva Krishna', informs us that only the northern part of the instrument was built in Jai Singh's day.[34] The southern sundial was only added during the reign of Maharaja Pratab Singh, a grandson of Jai Singh, when he had the whole building rebuilt.[35] During these alterations an internal room was built, decorated in the style of contemporary living rooms with stuccoed Mogul-style profiles. Today it is used as a storage room for astrolabes, telescopes and architectural models.

34 Line 6 of inscription.
35 In its original form, the Narivalaya Uttar Gola was presumably similar to the Kranti Writta Yantra. The Kranti Writta (see fig. 65) was never completed.
36 For a photo, see fig. 9 in 'Jantar Mantar' by the author in *du-Atlantis,* June 1966.

The Small Jai Prakash Yantra [36]

This is a hemisphere set into a low stone platform (fig. 50). It is made of pieces of marble and is open at the top. Its upper edge forms the horizontal plane. A string cross made of wire, whose point of intersection casts a shadow on to the spherical surface, connects the north, south, west and eastern points. This sunken stone hemisphere is a projection of the sky curving outwards above the horizontal plane. The lowest point of the

Fig. 49 The Narivalaya Uttar Gola Yantra (equatorial sundial), Jaipur. View of the south side of the sundial. The stonework of the sundial is painted bright yellow. The dial was made of red sandstone and white marble. On the north side there is a second dial which faces the north celestial pole.

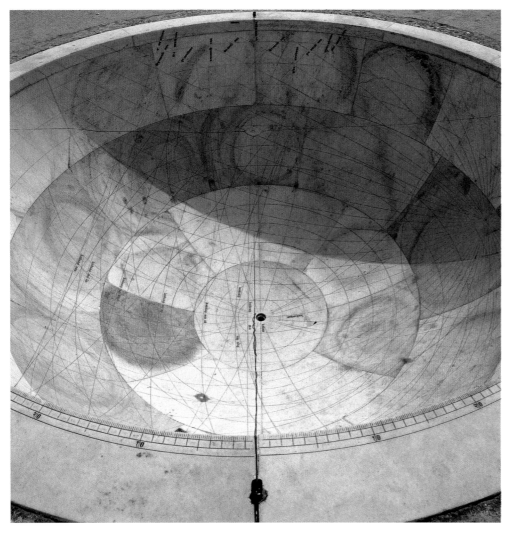

A second hemisphere, with the same diameter and likewise set into the platform, is known as the Kapali Yantra. It was not used for observing the sun and stars, serving purely as a model of the planetary orbits.

The Great Jai Prakash Yantras

The disadvantage of the Small Jai Prakash Yantra was obvious. The cross hairs showed a clear image of the daily path of the sun on the white inner surface of the hemisphere, but it was not possible to observe a star with this instrument. It would have been possible if they had been able to make the hemisphere out of a transparent material, but this was not technically feasible at that time. Jai Singh therefore took the spherical surface to pieces in the same way as he did for the circular surface and surrounding wall of the Rama Yantra: certain strips were omitted in one hemisphere and the gaps were made accessible from underground (figs. 51–53, 91) In a second instrument, the surfaces which appear here as gaps are made into graduated areas in such a way that the two hemispheres fit together to make a whole. The position of the gaps was not random of course. They are defined by large circles which intersect at the poles, that is lines of longitude at intervals of 15°.

They could now observe a star from the edges of the graduated area above the point of intersection of the cross hairs. One of the drawbacks of this instrument is that, as in the Rama Yantra, a star could only be observed if it had covered 15° of its orbit. Consequently, it has no graduation marks for minutes or seconds.

Fig. 50 Eastern Small Jai Prakash Yantra, Jaipur. The projection of the North Pole is on the right side of the concave marble structure. The horizontal circles represent zenith distances, i.e. altitudes.

hemisphere, exactly beneath the cross hairs, therefore represents the zenith. Concentric circles of altitude are engraved into the marble surface around this point and the large circles of an azimuthal scale intersect at it. The geographical latitude of Jaipur, on the meridian line taken from the southern point of the horizontal circle, produces the projected celestial north pole.

Concentric circles around this pole enable a direct reading of the declination of the sun to be taken. Large circles around the hemisphere which intersect at the pole complete the network of scales in such a way that the right ascension of the sun can also be read directly from the shadow of the cross hairs.

Fig. 51 Inside one of the Great Jai Prakash Yantras, Jaipur.

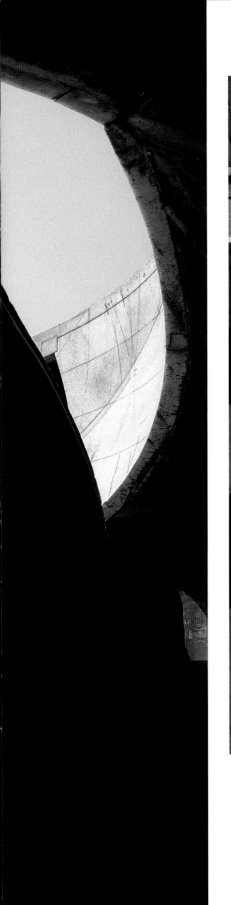

Fig. 53 *The Great Prakash Yantras (spherical instruments), Jaipur. View from the ground level down into the graduated area and the underground passages of the southernmost Great Jai Prakash Yantra. The spherical surface is a projection of the celestial vault. It permits measurements in the horizontal system (the zenith is situated in the bottom centre of the picture), as well as in the equatorial system (the concentric circles in the upper part of the picture are situated around the north celestial pole).*

Fig. 52 *The Great Prakash Yantras (spherical instruments), Jaipur. View from one of the underground passages leading to the hemispherical Jai Prakash Yantra, which is made of marble. Some strips were left out of the surface of the sphere so that an observer could run his eye along the edges of the concave marble surface.*

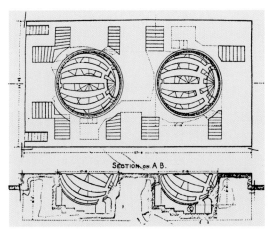

Fig. 55   View and section of the Great Jai Prakash Yantras in Jaipur as they were before repair work at the beginning of the 20th century (after G. R. Kaye).

Fig. 56   Model of the Great Jai Prakash Yantras in Jaipur, made for the Science Museum, London, in 1893.

37 See quotation p. 67.
38 See fig. 28.
39 Ms. London Or. 1977, fol. 66.

Fig. 54   The Rashi Valaya Yantras (ecliptical instruments; background) and a Jai Prakash Yantra (foreground) in Jaipur. The intriguing interplay of intersecting and overlapping circles, straight lines and triangles was not created for aesthetic reasons. These are in fact ancient Indian cosmic symbols.

Following pages
Fig. 58   The twelve Rashi Valaya Yantras (ecliptical instruments) in Jaipur, as seen from the Samrat Yantra (royal instrument), the highest of all the measuring instruments in the observatory (approximately 25 m high). These instruments are arranged in a zodiacal circle. When the corresponding sign appears on the horizon, the instrument's rising straight line points exactly to the pole of the ecliptic.

The Unnatansha Yantra

The Unnatansha Yantra (figs. 61, 93) is one of the few instruments of the Jaipur observatory which does not conform to Jai Singh's demands for large immovable structures.[37] It essentially consists of a free-hanging bronze ring which is held by a vertical and a horizontal strut. In the centre of the circle, where the struts intersect, there used to be a rotating sighting tube. The bronze circle was provided with graduation marks for determining the zenith distance or the altitude of any celestial body. In order also to be able to observe stars with a large zenith distance, they built a circular staircase around the bronze circle (there is also a similar type of staircase in an underground room in Tycho Brahe's observatory at Stjerneborg).[38]

It is surprising that Jai Singh decided to build this instrument, as around AD 1000 Al Biruni had stressed in his book *Al Quanun al Masudi*[39] that measurements taken with large rings lead to errors because the rings are so light they quickly loose their shape if they are placed upright or suspended.

Fig. 57   Model of the Unnatansha Yantra in Jaipur, made for the Science Museum, London, in 1893.

The Rashi Valaya Yantras

The Rashi Valaya Yantras (figs. 58, 89) are similar in construction to the Samrat Yantras, except that they include different angles with the horizon and point in different directions.

They were built because for astronomical calculation it is desirable not to first have to convert the readings usually taken on the horizon (azimuth and zenith distance) or the readings obtained on the equatorial plane (declination

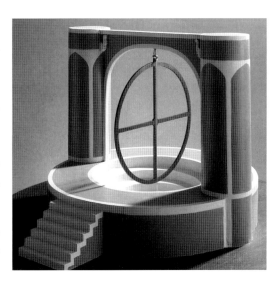

Fig. 60   By replacing traditional brass instruments with much larger masonry structures, Jai Singh was hoping for more precise astronomical data.

40 The Shastansha Yantra and the Dakshino Bhitti Yantra are also examples of building instruments which only allow measurements to be taken at a certain time, but which eliminate errors in orientation through being fixed.

Fig. 59   Virgo zodiacal sign, Rashi Valaya Yantra (ecliptical instrument), Jaipur. The Rashi Valaya Yantras were designed to measure the ecliptical latitude and longitude of a star.

and right ascension) to the most important reference frame of all, the ecliptic plane. This instrument was intended to enable all readings to be taken in the ecliptical system.

As a result of the obliquity of the ecliptic, an orbit around the celestial pole describes the pole of the ecliptic. Therefore what is needed is a movable instrument whose axis can be oriented at any time on the current position of the pole of the ecliptic. Alternatively, and this appeared to Jai Singh to be the right solution, one could build fixed instruments, each one of which by its fixed inclination towards the horizon and by its similarly fixed azimuthal orientation only points exactly to the pole of the ecliptic for a short moment.[40] It was thus decided to build twelve fixed ecliptical yantras in Jaipur, so that one of them could always be used for taking readings when the appropriate zodiacal animal of the twelve was beginning its diurnal (apparent) course across the sky on the horizon.

The Rashi Valaya Yantras were built symmetrically (apart from two exceptions) on a low platform serving as an artificial horizon. The

61   The Unnatansha Yantra consists of a bronze circle with a diameter
of about 5 metres. The graduation marks make it possible to determine
the altitude of stars.

62   The Small Samrat Yantra, Jaipur.
View of the white marble equatorial circle.

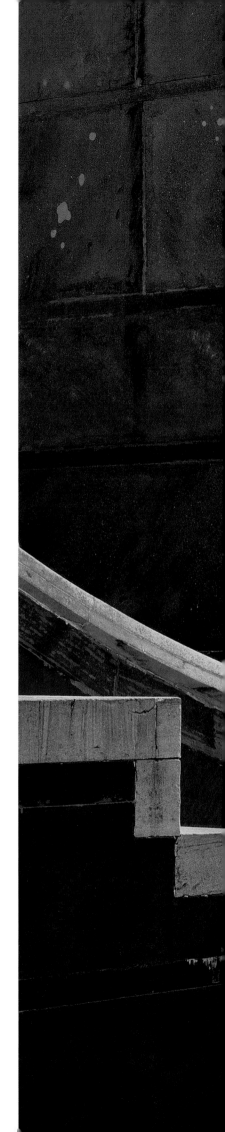

41 See historical photography in E. La Roche, *Indische Baukunst*, vol. 5, Munich, 1921, p. 171.
42 For a detailed discussion of the relative positions of the instruments, see p. 127ff.
43 William Hunter, 'Some Accounts of the Astronomical Labours of Jayasinha', in *Asiatic Researches*, vol. 5, 1799.
44 G. R. Kaye, *The Astronomical Observatories of Jai Singh*, Calcutta, 1918, p. 46.
45 Ibid.
46 A. Garrett and Ch. Guleri. *The Jaipur Observatory and its Builder*, Allahabad, 1902.
47 Gokul Chandra Bhawan, *Samrat Yantra*, Jaipur, n.d.

Aquarius and Gemini instruments, whose position destroys the symmetry, were moved to the south. There are two reasons for this irregularity: first, an existing circular building appears to have made it too difficult to divide the Rashi Valaya Yantras symmetrically;[41] and second, a triangular extension of the platform – partly made necessary by the different orientations of the surrounding wall and the alignment of the instruments – offered the possibility of avoiding the offending building by moving two of the instruments to the south.[42]

Fig. 64   *The Yantra Raja, Jaipur. The astrolabes made of brass were used to complement measurements taken by the larger stone instruments.*

History of the Jaipur Observatory

The sequence in which Jai Singh founded the observatories in Delhi, Jaipur, Mathura, Ujjain and Benares cannot be established for certain because of a lack of historical documentary evidence. From the *Zig Muhammad Shahi*,[43] however, it emerges that Jai Singh built the observatories of Jaipur, Mathura, Ujjain and Benares in order to check the measuring data obtained in Delhi, proving that the latter was built first. Kaye[44] and Sayet Ahmad Khan[45] state that it was founded in 1724, Garrett[46] and Gokul Chandra Bhawan[47] on the other hand say 1710. The observatory in the palace at Jaipur, according to documentary evidence, was completed in 1734, six years after the foundation of the town.

From Tieffenthaler's description of the observatory, it emerges that the Rashi Valaya Yantra, Dakshino Bhitti Yantra, Narivalaya Uttar Gola Yantra, Shastansha Yantra and Unnatansha Yantra instruments were definitely built during Jai Singh's lifetime. By the 'horizontal sundial carved into a very large stone', Tieffenthaler means the square platform which contains the standard measure for the instruments in the form of an east-west and a north-south line. It is described as 'Jai Singh's Seat' (fig. 86).

Its circular scale surrounding the straight lines which point to the compass points was originally fashioned in plaster stucco and was only replaced by a stone scale in 1876. The radius of the circle corresponds to the radius of the quadrants of the Great Samrat Yantra. From this Garrett concluded that the individual pieces of marble on the quadrants were measured here.

Tieffenthaler was certainly wrong when he described Jai Singh's Seat as a horizontal sundial, since if this were the case the graduated scales would be pointless. A model of the whole observatory, built at the beginning of the 20th century for the Deutsches Museum in Munich, unfortunately also shows the platform as a sundial with a gnomon in the centre.

It was not only the restoration of Jai Singh's Seat which took place in 1876. Maharaja Ram Singh also had the Small Samrat Yantra built. In addition, according to Garrett the Dakshino Bhitti Yantra, originally situated on the west side of the courtyard, was demolished and rebuilt

Fig. 63   *The Small Samrat Yantra, Jaipur. This small instrument of red sandstone and white marble, the preferred material in Mogul architecture, was built by one of Jai Singh's 19th-century successors and was based on the Great Samrat Yantra. Here, too, the sloping surface points to the northern celestial pole and marble quadrants represent the equator.*

Fig. 65 *The Kranti Writta, Jaipur. This measuring instrument was never completed. It could be used as an equatorial sundial, or else, with the addition of a few movable metal circles, as an instrument for measuring the ecliptical latitude and longitude of a star.*

stone by stone on its present-day site. This re-siting is said to have been necessary because of a new road being built inside the palace grounds. Even today, a road on the north-west corner of the courtyard cuts off a part of the rectangular ground plan.

Most of the instruments quickly deteriorated over the following decades. Old photographs show only foundations and ruins. There would probably be no trace of them at all if the ruling maharaja had not decided to restore all the in-struments to their original condition in 1901. He appointed Garrett and Chimanlal to supervise the work, and Chandradhar Guleri,[48] Mali Ram and Gokul Chandra Bhawan[49] to carry it out. It is to the restorers' credit that they replaced the plaster graduations with marble. The plaster stucco only ever survived a few monsoons. (As a result, in Delhi, where not all the scales were replaced, the Jai Prakash Yantras are now in such bad condition that we can only guess at their original form.

At the time of the restoration work, the Great Jai Prakash Yantras in Jaipur appeared to be nearly in ruins. Therefore, it was decided to wall up ten staircases which led from the platform into the underground rooms and corridors and to make the instrument accessible only through two new staircases to the east and west of the platform.

A few years ago, the present maharaja of Jaipur handed over part of his palace to the government of Rajasthan. The observatory is situated in this area. The current costs can obviously not be borne by the government and as a result the grounds and instruments are no longer maintained to the standard required.

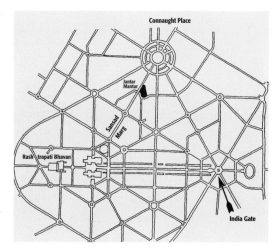

Fig. 66   City map of New Delhi.

2.2   THE INSTRUMENTS OF THE DELHI OBSERVATORY

The Delhi observatory, known as the Jantar Mantar (meaning 'magic sign'; see glossary), was built on a broad, treeless plain some distance from the city walls. Only when the English founded a new royal seat for the viceroy, designed by Sir Edwin Lutyens, did the observatory come to be absorbed into New Delhi's massive housing development.

In his prologue to the astronomical tables, the *Zig Muhammad Shahi*, Jai Singh writes about the founding of the observatory:

He [Jai Singh] built here [in Delhi] several instruments for an observatory as they had been built in Samarkand … In so doing, it became clear to him that the brass instruments did not come up to his standards of accuracy. This was due to their small size, the lack of any division into minutes, the wear and tear on their axes, the inaccuracy of the centres of the circles and finally the poor construction of all the planes which were always unstable. He could see that for precisely these reasons the readings of the Ancients, Hipparchus and Ptolomy, for example, were shown to be inaccurate. Therefore, in Dar-ul-khelafet Shah Jahanabad [Delhi], which is at the centre of the empire and kingdom, he built instruments which he had invented himself, such as the Jai Prakash Yantra, for example, the Rama Yantra and the Samrat Yantra, whose radius amounts to 18 cubits (or gaz) and in which one minute of an arc corresponds to the size of one and a half barleycorns. These instruments are made of stone and limestone, of excellent durability, designed according to the rules of geometry and suited to the geographical latitude of the place and its meridian. In this way inaccuracies of measurement were avoided and the correct way to build an observatory discovered.[50]

In Delhi, a Great Samrat Yantra, two Jai Prakash Yantras and a Mishra Yantra have survived. But it emerges from Hunter's account (1799) that there was originally also a Dakshino Bhitti Yantra used for observing celestial bodies in their meridian transit.[51]

48 According to Gokul Chandra Bhawan.
49 Author of *Samrat Yantra*.
50 Maharaja Jai Singh II *Zig Muhammad Shahi*, Jaipur, n.d., translated into English by William Hunter.
51 William Hunter, 'Some Accounts of the Astronomical Labours of Jayasinha', in *Asiatic Researches*, vol. 5, 1799.

Fig. 67 New Delhi, view from the
Mishra Yantra looking towards the Samrat
Yantra (foreground), the Jai Prakash Yantra
and one of the Rama Yantras (background).

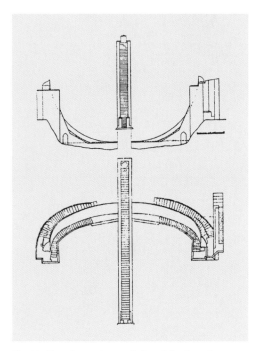

Fig. 68 Elevation and ground plan of the Great Samrat Yantra in New Delhi (after G. R. Kaye).

The Great Samrat Yantra

As in Jaipur, the observatory in Delhi is dominated by the Samrat Yantra, which is visible from a distance. It has similar dimensions and works in a similar way to the Great Samrat Yantra in Jaipur, apart from the fact that a second Shastansha Yantra was not installed in the west tower. The Shastansha Yantra in the east tower is in ruins and its entrances were walled up in 1909. But today it is possible to look into the inside of the Shastansha Yantra from the roof of the east tower because part of the ceiling has fallen in.

As in Jaipur, the Shastansha Yantra was built in a wide pit. The drainage system, however, did not work as efficiently as in Jaipur and the pit filled with water. As a result, the quadrant's graduated scales, which were made of plaster, have been partially destroyed.

Fig. 69 Samrat Yantra and Mishra Yantra (in background), aquatint by T. and W. Daniell, 1799, made with the aid of a camera obscura.

Fig. 71 *Samrat Yantra, New Delhi. Steps running alongside the scales on the two quadrants make it possible to carry out detailed measurements to determine the coordinates of a star.*

Fig. 70 *Mishra Yantra, New Delhi. The measuring scales of the Mishra Jantra are made of marble. They are subdivided into degrees, minutes and seconds.*

The Jai Prakash Yantras

To the south, two Jai Prakash Yantras, now partially collapsed, adjoin the Samrat Yantra. As far as we can tell, they are similar to those at Jaipur. The two hemispherical faces onto which the sky was projected are not made of marble like those in Jaipur, but of plaster. Neither are they set into a common platform. Each one rises up above the ground surrounded by its own building. Inside the building are some undecorated store-rooms and some living rooms stuccoed in the Mogul style, with windows, storage niches and doors. Only the eastern Jai Prakash Yantra has a cellar. Steep, narrow stairs lead from the entrance halls of the north and south ground-floor rooms into the basement. Because the drainage system of the observatory was unfinished – and the water table may have risen – the cellars are flooded.

Fig. 72 Inside the Western Jai Prakash Yantra, New Delhi. The original scales are made of plaster and are in poor condition today.

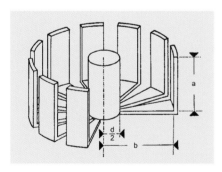

Fig. 73 Diagram of the Rama Yantra in New Delhi.

Pages 76–77 Fig. 75 The northern
Rama Yantra (drum-shaped sundial),
New Delhi. The gnomon which casts
the shadow is situated in the
centre. The azimuthal direction of the
sun is calculated by halving its shadow.

The Rama Yantras

South of the Jai Prakash Yantras are two drum-shaped buildings in stone which, like the Rama Yantras in Jaipur, were used for establishing azimuth and zenith distances. Although these huge buildings have much the same function as those in Jaipur, they appear heavier, older and more monumental.

A mighty pillar, built of plaster-covered stone, towers up in the centre of each of the Rama Yantras in Delhi. This serves not only as the geometrical centre but also, thanks to its continuous

Fig. 74 View south from the top of the Samrat Yantra over one of the Jai Prakash Yantras (foreground) and the Rama Yantras (background), New Delhi.

74

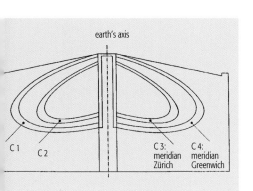

earth's axis

C1   C2   C3:   C4:
            meridian   meridian
            Zürich   Greenwich

Fig. 76 Diagram of the Mishra Yantra.

cylindrical shape, as the visual point of repose in the endless circular movement of the sector-shaped graduated areas and the surrounding circular wall, which is broken up by keel arches. There is no such visual centre in the Rama Yantras in Jaipur. The kinetic energy created at the centre peters out inconsequentially into a thin metal stick, which is at odds formally with the surrounding stone graduated areas.

It was not only in the pillar that the architect in Delhi, playing with a small number of basic architectural shapes, continued to use the existing style right down to the smallest details. The arched foundations of the stone sectors of the circle also illustrate the stylistic uniformity. The Jaipur building cannot compete with the one in Delhi in this respect either, since in Jaipur the sectors of the circle are only supported by thin rectangular stone posts and do not contribute to any specific architectural form. These differences in design and quality rule out any possibility that the buildings in Jaipur and Delhi were designed by the same architects or at the same time. According to Garrett, the Rama Yantras of Jaipur were not actually built in their present form until the renovation work in 1891. In their original form, all the graduated areas were made of plaster, which would inevitably result in a completely different shape of building.

In the Rama Yantra in Delhi (fig. 73), angles could be measured in the following way: the azimuth of the sun was obtained by halving the broad shadow which the stone pillar casts on the scales. The end of the shadow indicated its zenith distance. A piece of string could be attached to the centre of the circular surface forming the top of the stone pillar. It dangled over the edge of this circular surface and, for observing stars, as in Jaipur, it served as a sighting aid for the observer, who moved the other end of the string along the graduation marks of the sectors of the circle. If they wanted to measure zenith distances of more than 45° then they had to take the string up along the vertical graduated areas of the circular

wall. For this purpose, steps were provided at irregular intervals in the niches between the scales.

This meant that the height of the circular wall above the sectors of the circle (a) corresponds to the radius (b) minus half the diameter of the column in the centre (fig. 73).

The Mishra Yantra

A wall situated in the meridian plane serves as the plane of symmetry for this 'mixed instrument'. The celestial pole can be observed along the upper edge of the wall, which is inclined towards the horizontal plane at the same angle as the hypotenuse of the Samrat Yantra.[52] On both sides of the wall rising to the north, marble scales extend out in a semicircle. Their central points lie on the edges of the hypotenuse. The marble circles are supported by curved walls.

The earliest frequently quoted account of the way the Mishra Yantra works is by Gokul Chandra Bhawan.[53] He attributed the circles C1 to C4 to various local meridians as follows:

C1:   One can see the sun from here at 6.52 (local time), when it is 12.00 noon in Natke, a little place in Japan.

C2:   One can see the sun from here at 7.24 when it is 12.00 noon in Syrichev on the island of Piknam.

C3:   One can see the sun from here at 16.36, when it is 12.00 noon in Zürich in Italy where there is an observatory.

Fig. 77 The central semi-circles of the Mishra Yantra in New Delhi are flanked by quadrants (foreground) which are parallel to the equator.

Pages 80–81
Fig. 78 Mishra Yantra seen from the south.

52 In accordance with the geographical latitude of Delhi 28° 37' 35".
53 Gokul Chandra Bhawan, *Samrat Yantra*, Jaipur, n.d.

Fig. 79   Aquatint made by T. & W. Daniell in 1799 showing the Great Samrat Yantra (foreground) and the Rama Yantra (background).

marked on a map, far less had a well-known observatory. If we compare the times given, it is quite obvious that these two circles are simply mirror images of the eastern half of the instrument and do not fulfil any measuring function. In the case of Zürich and Syrichev, moreover, the mirror images appear to have been linked together by their similar sound. Such deliberate non-functional duplication is characteristic of Hindu ideas of harmony. One only needs to recall the observatories in Delhi and Benares, 'Jantar Mantar' and 'Man-Mandir'.

In his book about Jai Singh's work, Kaye, who also adopted Gokul Chandra Bhawan's dubious theory, gave the readings above for the marble circles, to which we have added the measurements taken by the author and some local information. The different values could be the result of the constant restoration work on the Mishra Yantra and are thus not mutually exclusive.

The two halves of a Samrat Yantra are situated on both sides of the Mishra Yantra. An additional quadrant on the west side is obviously not used for measuring. A small Dakshino Bhitti Yantra is also set into the east side.

The following sources are available for dating the Mishra Yantra: at the beginning of the *Zig Muhammad Shahi* in 1728[55] Jagannath makes no mention of the Mishra Yantra in his list of instruments; Jai Singh died in 1743;[56] the observatory in Zürich was founded in 1759,[57] and Hunter saw the Mishra Yantra in 1799.[58] It is thus possible to deduce that the building was probably built between 1759 and 1799, presumably in the reign of Jai Singh's successor, Maharaja Madho Singh (1751–65), who people say was attempting to continue the work of his father.

To the south-west of the Mishra Yantra are two thick columns on an irregular ground plan. Traditionally it is said that, on the day of the winter solstice, no shadow is cast from one to the other. In fact, these are the ruined walls of various gateway arches which can still be seen in a 19th-century representation of the observatory.[59] This

C 4:   One can see the sun from here at 17.08 when it is 12.00 noon in Greenwich in England, where there is an observatory.

54 It is not known what purpose the meridian of Zürich might have served for Jai Singh, since his European collaborators were Portuguese and their astronomical tables related to the observatory of Lisbon.

55 William Hunter, 'Some Accounts of the Astronomical Labours of Jayasinha', in *Asiatic Researches,* vol. 5, 1799.

56 According to James Tod, *Annals and Antiquities of Rajasthan,* vol. 2, London, 1832.

57 According to G. R. Kaye, *The Astronomical Observatories of Jai Singh,* Calcutta, 1918.

58 See William Hunter, 'Some Accounts of the Astronomical Labours of Jayasinha', in *Asiatic Researches,* vol. 5, 1799.

59 This picture (reproduced on page 1) comes from the museum in the Red Fort in Delhi.

60 'Description des Monuments de Delhi', in *Journal Asiatique,* Dec. 1860.

61 According to Gokul Chandra Bhawan, *Samrat Yantra,* Jaipur, n.d.

62 R. Barker, 'An Account of the Bramin's Observatory at Benares', in *Philosophical Transactions of the Royal Society of London,* vol. 67, part II, London, 1777, p. 599f.

Circle	Angles according to the local data	Angles measured in Kaye's time	Angles measured by the author in 1968
1	77°16′	77°18′	77°18′23″
2	68°34′	69°50′	67°34′36″
3	68°01′	68°42′	68°54′33″
4	77°22′	77°22′	79°57′07″

This interpretation of these circular scales is flawed in several ways (in addition to the erroneous siting of Zürich in Italy). Circle 4 corresponds with amazing accuracy to the local meridian of Greenwich; and circle 3 to the meridian of Zürich, with an insignificant difference of one degree.[54] But it appears to be quite impossible for circles 1 and 2 to realistically relate to two places in East Asia, since they are not even

charge of construction work; Chandu Lal, Bhagirat and Gokul Chandra Bhawan[61] were site supervisers.

Kaye visited the observatory in Delhi in 1915 and 1916. From his suggestion that they replace the plaster circular scales on the Niyat Chakra Yantra by marble ones, we can conclude that much more restoration work was carried out at a later date. The Niyat Chakra Yantra was the only instrument at the Mishra Yantra to be given the marble scales suggested by Kaye. At the same time, a garden was laid out around the instruments in the style of the Mogul period and the observatory was separated from the surrounding residential areas and road by a perimeter wall. It is not known when this work was done.

2.3 THE OBSERVATORY IN BENARES

Jai Singh had the Benares observatory built on the roof of the Manmandir Palace ('Palace of Man-Singh'), which belonged to the maharaja of Jaipur and is situated on the banks of the Ganges (figs. 83, 85). Sir Robert Barker visited it in 1772 and wrote in a letter to Sir John Pringle:[62]

Fig. 80 The observatory on the roof of the Manmandir Palace, built in 1710, is in a poor condition today.

picture also shows the extent of damage to all the instruments, which is already mentioned in the 'Description des Monuments de Delhi en 1852':[60]

> Today this observatory lies in ruins, all the instruments are cracked and all traces of the measuring lines have disappeared. No useful conclusions can be drawn from any of the instruments. Three of the stone and mortar instruments still survive in a broken and damaged state.

Repair work was started in the same year, but it was halted a year later because the maharaja of Jaipur did not have enough money to restore it to its original condition. It was not until 1910, after the successful restoration of the Jaipur buildings by Garrett, that work in Delhi got underway in 1910. The engineer C. E. Estatherd was in overall

> We entered this building [Manmandir] and went up a staircase to the top of a part of it, near to the river Ganges, that led to a large terrace, where, to my surprise and satisfaction, I saw a number of instruments yet remaining, in the greatest preservation, stupendously large, immoveable from the spot, and built of stone, some of them being upwards of twenty feet in height; and, although they are said to have been erected two hundrd years ago, the graduations and divisions on the several arcs appeared as well cut, and as accurately divided, as if they had been the performance of a modern artist.

Fig. 81 *View across the Ganges to the observatory on the roof of the Manmandir Palace at Benares.*

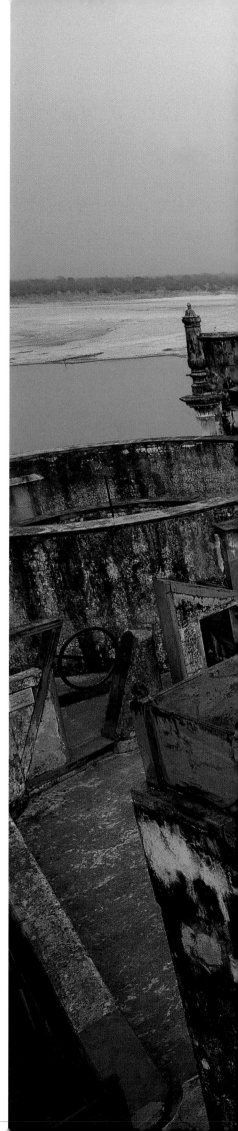

Fig. 82 *The observatory on the roof of the Manmandir Palace. Jai Singh selected this extraordinary location for an observatory because at the time the horizon was not obstructed by any other buildings.*

Fig. 83 *The observatory on the Manmandir in Benares, 18th-century engraving.*

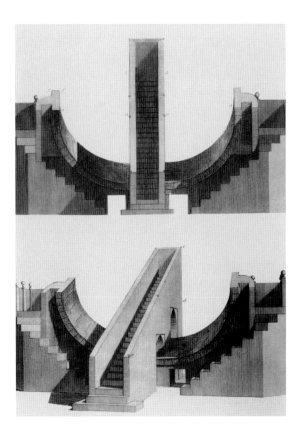

Fig. 84 The Great Samrat Yantra in the Benares observatory (top, elevation; bottom, view from south-east), 18th-century engraving.

This observatory at Benares is said to have been built by the order of the emperor ACK-BAR; for as this wise prince endeavoured to improve the arts, so he wished also to recover the sciences of Hindostan, and therefore directed that three such places should be erected; one at Delhi, another at Agra, and the third at Benares.

This letter is valuable, since Sir Robert Barker saw the instruments a few decades after Jai Singh's death when they were presumably still in their original state. The information which he had received about the supposed patron, however, was erroneous. There is no doubt that Jai Singh was the architect. Several authors give 1737 as the year of foundation. An inscription on the Samrat Yantra, presumably added in 1911 by the restorers, however, suggests that the observatory had already been laid out in 1710.

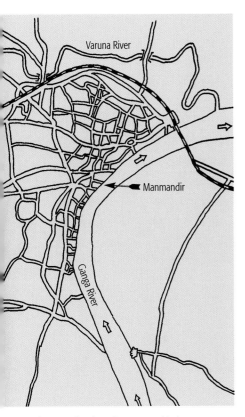

Fig. 85   City plan of Benares with the Manmandir Palace by the Ganges River.

The observatory in Benares is on a much smaller scale than the observatories in Delhi and Jaipur, because the size of the instruments and their weight were limited by the dimensions of the roof terrace and the load-bearing capacity of the palace walls. There is a large Samrat Yantra on an almost square roof surface (fig. 84), while a later rectangular terrace above a narrower wing of the building supports the Narivalaya Dakshino, Uttar Gola, Chakra Yantra, Digamsa Yantra and Small Samrat Yantra. For some reason, the patron or the astronomers felt that it was necessary to give the Digamsa Yantra a circumference which exceeded the width of the roof-space available, and so the roof terrace was extended by means of a projecting structure to the north-east.

Since the Manmandir is not oriented on the compass points but is aligned with the façades on the banks of the Ganges, the position of the instruments was set at an angle to the ground plan in a similar way to Jaipur. This difference in orientation, as well as a slope leading to the extension of the terrace in the north-eastern part, lends a somewhat random impression to the observatory. It is difficult to identify any systematic arrangement in the many different directions and slopes.[63]

The instruments work in the same way as those in Delhi or Jaipur. The observatory is structurally sound, but the paintwork, which has not been renewed for years, gives the complex a dilapidated look (fig. 82). The upper storeys of the Manmandir are uninhabited.

2.4   THE OBSERVATORY IN UJJAIN

Today Ujjain is an insignificant little town situated halfway between Delhi and Bombay, but in Jai Singh's day it was the capital of the province of Malwa. In 1721, the Mogul Muhammad Shah appointed Jai Singh as governor of Malwa[64] and it is no surprise that he later built an observatory here, since Ujjain had been at the centre of Hindu astronomy for centuries.

According to Hindu cosmological ideas, the meridian of Ujjain runs through the centre of the world. For that reason, all their astronomical calculations were focused on this place; this is somewhat similar to the English making the Greenwich meridian and the French the Paris meridian into the line of reference for taking their readings.

Father Tieffenthaler was the first European to write about the instruments in Ujjain:

Ujen, the capital of Malwa, is a very large, heavily populated and built-up town on a large plain … There are also two very large lakes in the town; one at the ox market, the other, known as Garsathi, and charmingly situated to the south-west, is full of water-birds and has several bays. Not far away is the suburb built by King Jesing, former governor of this province, which is alongside an observatory and other equipment constructed of mortar; there are, for instance, two equinoctial sundials, an upper and a lower one; a wall whose upper edge forms an angle with the horizontal plane equal to the local latitude pointing towards the pole and situated on the meridian, with a geometrical quadrant on both sides; in addition there is a limestone gnomon and a meridian line engraved in stone.[65]

A detailed description of the individual instruments can be found in Hunter's report of 1799.[66] Even in those days he mentions that some circular scales have been damaged by the weather. When Kaye came to Ujjain in 1915 or 1916, he found only ruins.[67] He writes:

The observatory now consists of the following instruments:

63 This fact obviously caused the producer of the plans in Kaye's book so many difficulties that he drew the site plan very badly. Presumably his drawings are based not on exact measurements, but on an unreliable memory and a few rough sketches.

64 According to James Tod, *Annals and Antiquities of Rajasthan*, vol. 2, London, 1832.

65 Translated from the German translation of Joseph Tieffenthaler's work by J. Bernoulli, *Beschreibung von Hindustan*, Berlin, 1785, p. 246.

66 See William Hunter, 'Some Accounts of the Astronomical Labours of Jayasinha', in *Asiatic Researches*, vol. 5, 1799.

67 Photos in G. R. Kaye, *The Astronomical Observatories of Jai Singh*, Calcutta, 1918.

a) The Samrat Yantra.
b) The Dakshino Vritti Yantra.
c) The Nari Valaya Yantra.
d) The Digamsa Yantra.

These are all in a state of ruin. The foundations of the Digamsa Yantra have evidently moved, and its walls are badly cracked. The Dakshinovritti Yantra is inclined to the perpendicular at an angle of about 5 degrees. This is possibly due to the faulty structure, for the foundations of this heavy mass of masonry seem to be inadequate. The Samrat Yantra is in a dilapidated state, and the styles and graduation have disappeared from the Nari Valaya.[68]

In form and function, the instruments are similar to those in the other observatories. They are only of minor importance for our study because, in accordance with Kaye's detailed suggestions for restoration, they were rebuilt from scratch by the Archaeological Survey of India.

2.5   THE OBSERVATORY IN MATHURA

This observatory has disappeared without trace, so the description by Father Tieffenthaler, who visited it in the middle of the 18th century, is particularly valuable.

The town [Mathura] itself is surrounded by a rampart and is ruled by the Jats; it was formerly ruled by the Raja of Jepor, to whom the Mongolian emperor had handed over the government of the town. It is situated on this side of the Jemna [Jumna].

A castle built by a certain very rich Mohammedan towers up amidst all the dilapidated buildings; it is situated on a hill from which one looks down on to an immeasurably large plain. On the top of the castle you can see astronomical instruments made by the famous amateur astronomer, Raja Jesing; particularly noteworthy is a limestone gnomon standing 12 foot high and depicting the axis of the celestial sphere; in addition, there is an equinoctial sundial five spans in diameter alongside another smaller one built on the local latitude. Other instruments represent various segments of the sphere. In general, this observatory is a sort of replica of the one in Jepor: but it is superior to this with regard to its high situation and the broad plain which it dominates, even if it is inferior in other ways; for in the one in Jepor which is situated on flat ground, the rising and setting of stars can be seen only on the enormously high limestone gnomon. The castle itself, which has a large circumference and is surrounded by strong walls, has the Jemna [Jumna] as its moat to the east and is like a mountain created artificially out of stone.[69]

68 Ibid.
69 Translated from the German translation of Joseph Tieffenthaler's work by J. Bernoulli, *Beschreibung von Hindustan*, Berlin, 1785, p. 143.

Plans 1 | The observatory of Jai Singh in Jaipur, built 1734
26°55′ 27.4″ north

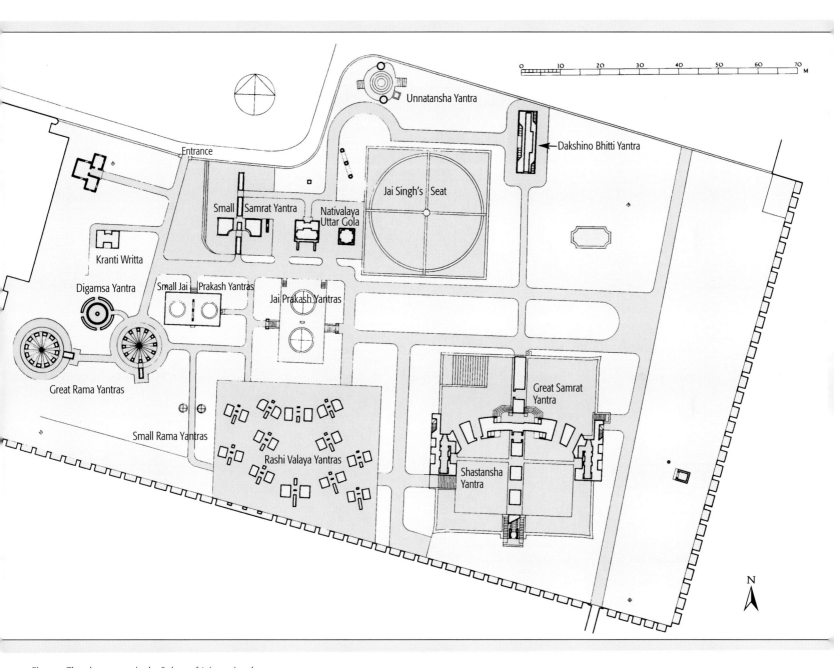

Unnatansha Yantra

Dakshino Bhitti Yantra

Entrance

Jai Singh's Seat

Small Samrat Yantra

Nativalaya Uttar Gola

Kranti Writta

Digamsa Yantra

Small Jai Prakash Yantras

Jai Prakash Yantras

Great Rama Yantras

Great Samrat Yantra

Small Rama Yantras

Rashi Valaya Yantras

Shastansha Yantra

N

Fig. 86 The observatory in the Palace of Jaipur, site plan.

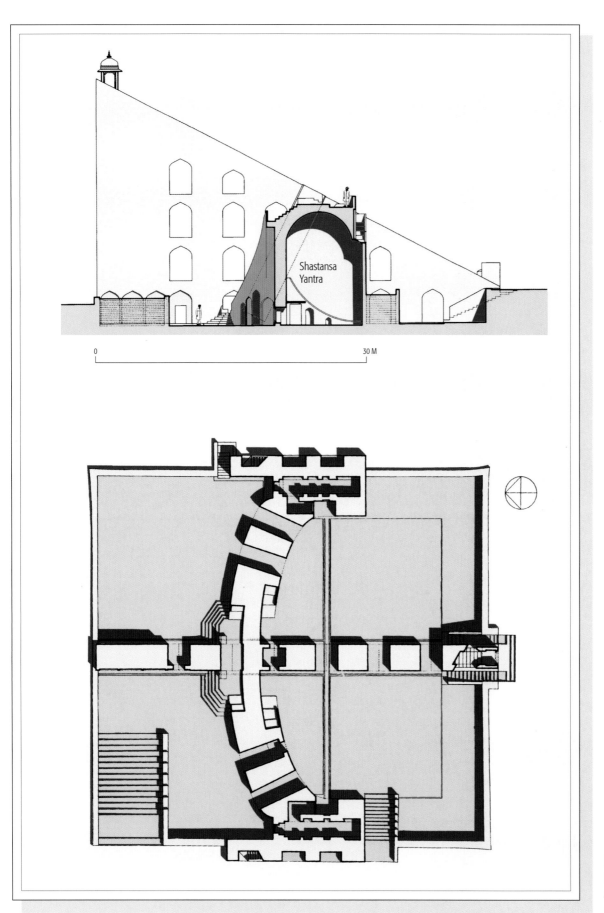

Shastansa
Yantra

0   30 M

Fig. 87   Great Samrat
Yantra, Jaipur,
section through the west tower
(top) and ground plan (bottom).

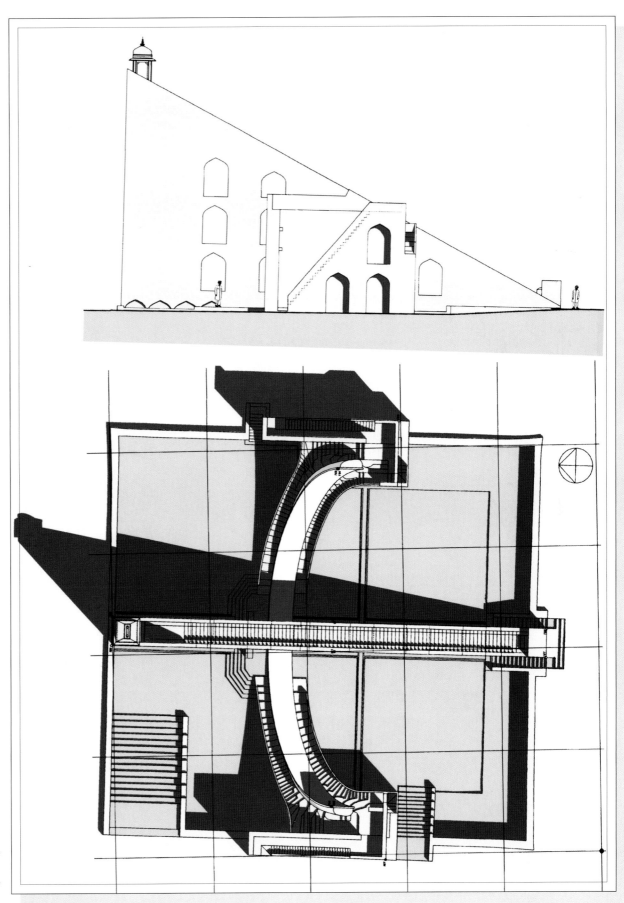

Fig. 88 Great Samrat Yantra, Jaipur, west elevation (top) and top view (bottom).

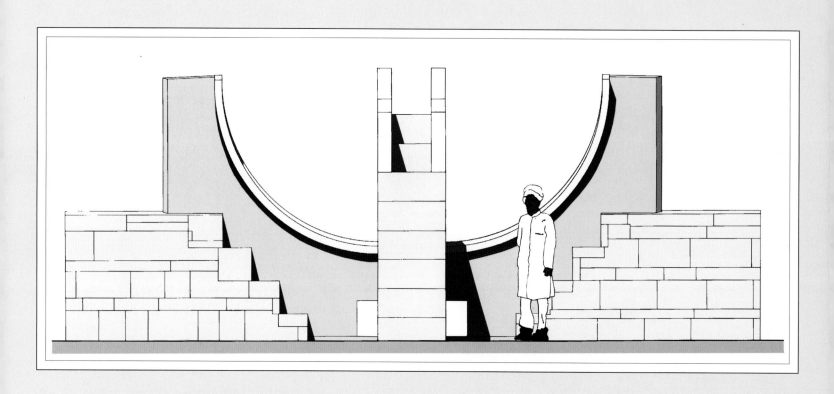

Pages 92–94
Fig. 89   Rashi Valaya Yantra, Jaipur,
Cancer zodiacal sign, south elevation (left)
and top view (right).

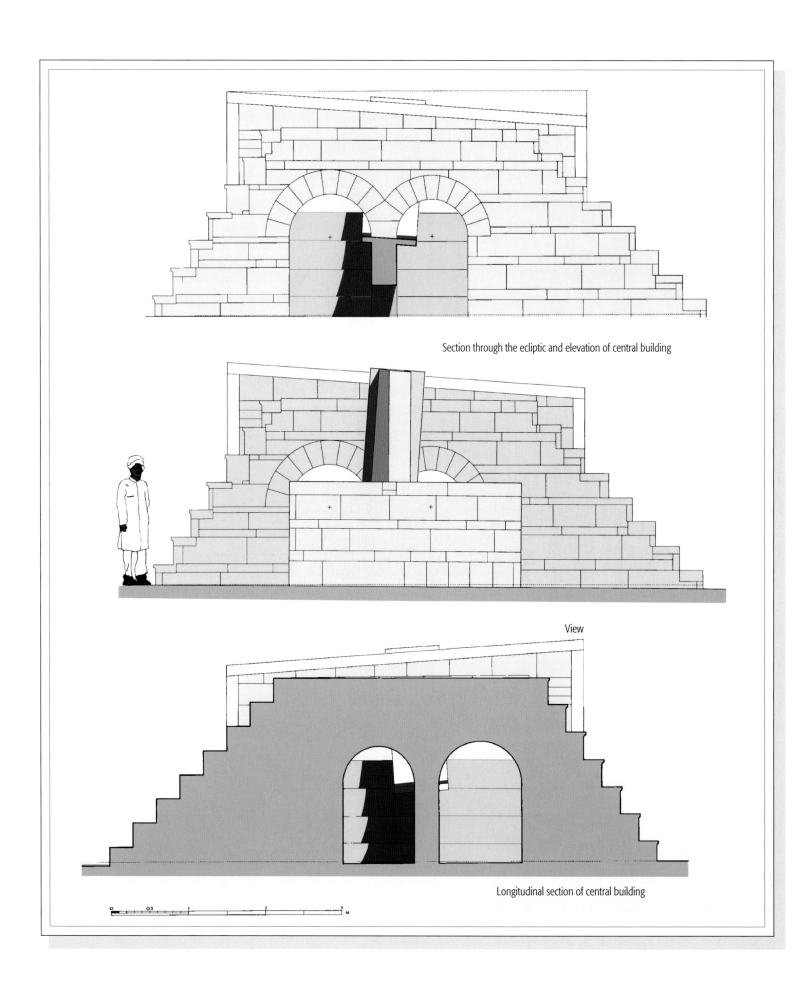

Section through the ecliptic and elevation of central building

View

Longitudinal section of central building

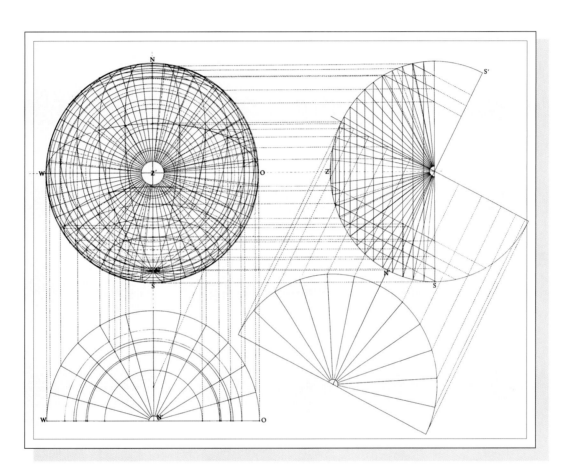

Fig. 91   The geometrical division of the Jai Prakash Yantra, Jaipur.

Fig. 90   Rashi Valaya Yantra, Jaipur,
Cancer zodiacal sign, elevation and sections.

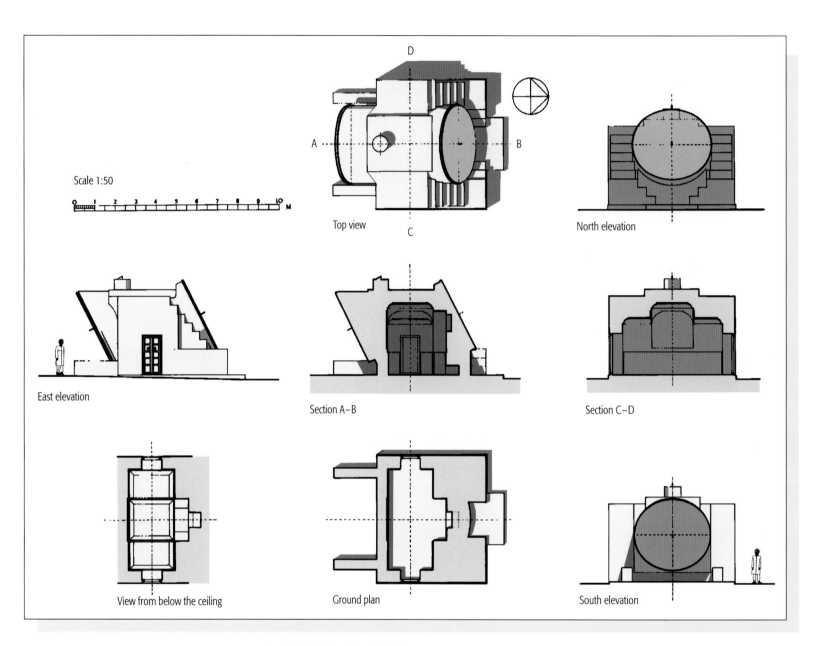

Scale 1:50

Top view

North elevation

East elevation

Section A–B

Section C–D

View from below the ceiling

Ground plan

South elevation

Fig. 92   Narivalaya Uttar Gola, Jaipur.

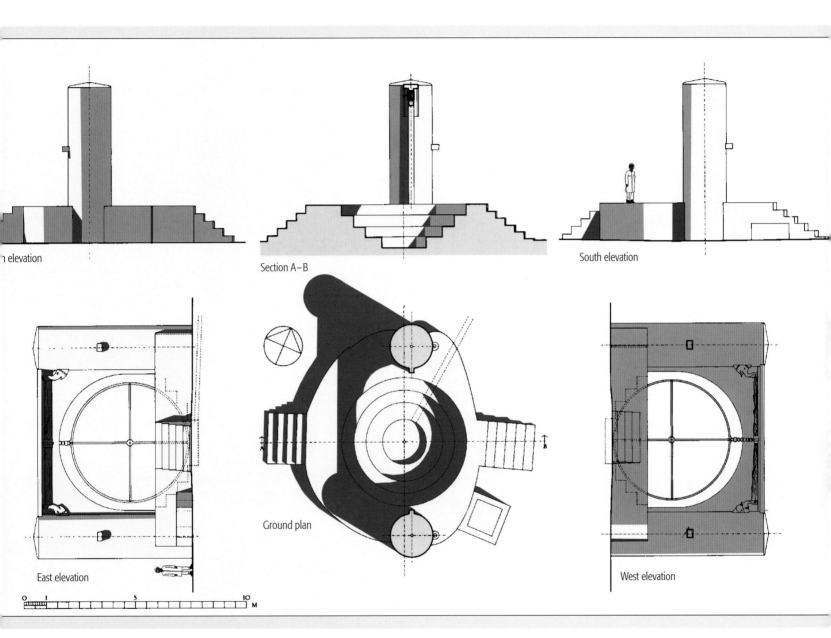

elevation

Section A–B

South elevation

East elevation

Ground plan

West elevation

Fig. 93   Unnatansha Yantra, Jaipur.

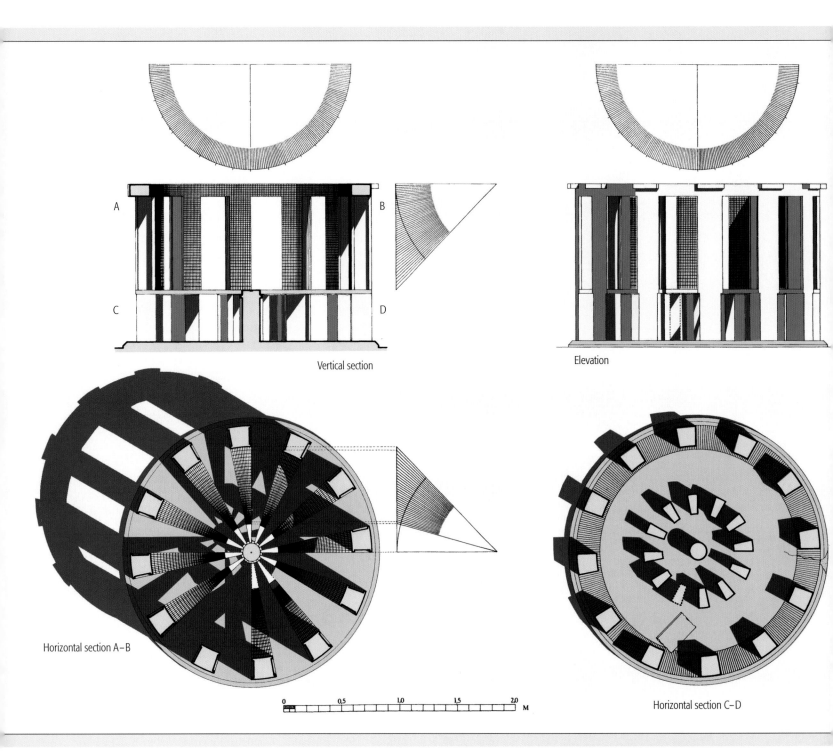

Vertical section

Elevation

Horizontal section A–B

Horizontal section C–D

0   0,5   1,0   1,5   2,0   M

Fig. 94   Small Rama Yantra, Jaipur, Eastern building.

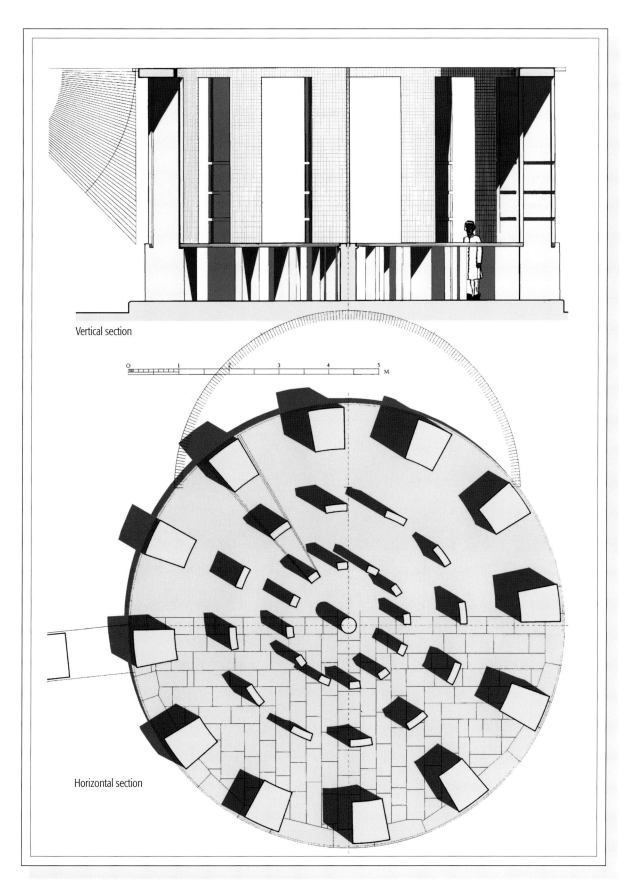

Vertical section

Horizontal section

Fig. 95   *Great Eastern Rama Yantra, Jaipur, section and ground plan.*

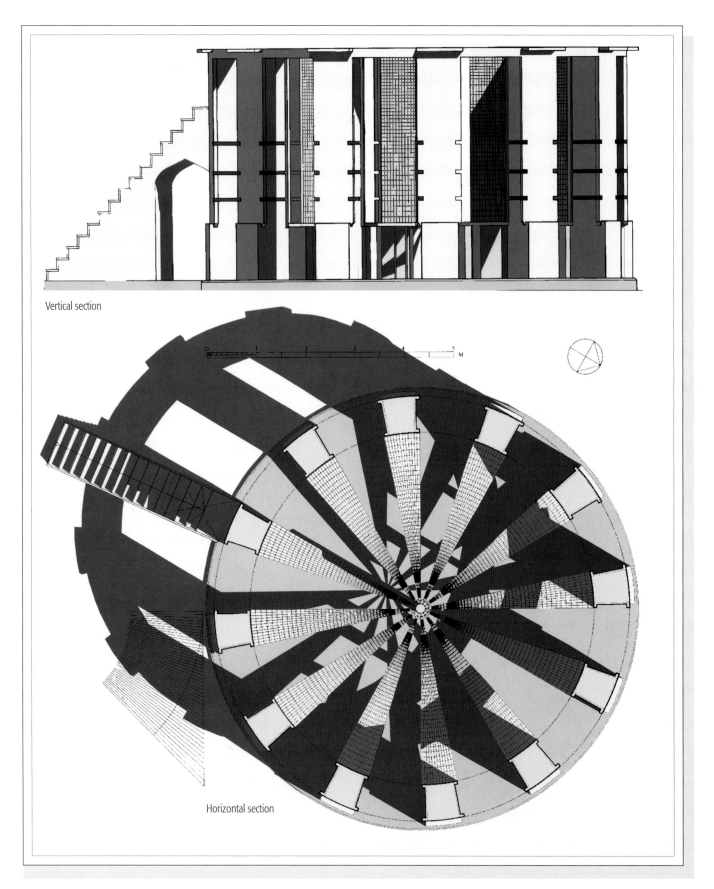

Vertical section

Horizontal section

Fig. 96   Great Eastern Rama Yantra, Jaipur, vertical and horizontal section

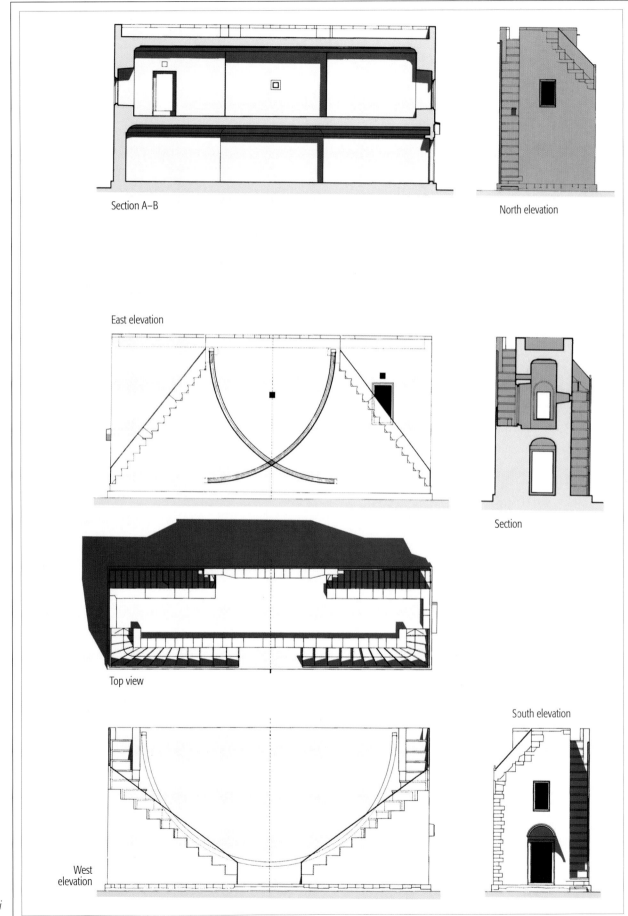

Section A–B

North elevation

East elevation

Section

Top view

South elevation

West elevation

Fig. 97   Dakshino Bhitti Yantra, Jaipur.

3 | A New Attempt at Interpretation

Fig. 98 View of one of the marble quadrants of the Great Samrat Yantra, Jaipur. There is a smooth transition from the sunny area to the shady one.

From the preface to Jai Singh's[70] astronomical tables it emerges that, in addition to the five built, the maharaja intended to build more observatories in other provincial centres within his jurisdiction. He gives as his reason for this huge undertaking the fact that he wanted to give everyone who felt inclined to study the stars the opportunity to do so. Such enthusiasm is surprising, especially as Jai Singh's building programme was almost as costly as the efforts of the imperial house. In addition, it must have been clear to Jai Singh and his collaborators that, contrary to his expectations, the accuracy of the readings showed no improvement as the size of the instruments increased.

In Jaipur, for example, there is a small metal Samrat Yantra (fig. 60) next to the large stone Samrat Yantra. If we observe the sun's shadow which the 'hypotenuse' casts on the quadrants of both instruments, then it becomes apparent that the small metal instrument produces results which are every bit as good as the large one. In both cases, there is a smooth transition from the area in shadow to the area in the sun and the edge can be all the more difficult to define the bigger the radius of the quadrants or the greater the distance between the edge casting the shadow and the image of the shadow (fig. 98).

This fact can be explained by the diameter of the sun's sphere. Its light does not come from one single point, but from a disc whose diameter is around 30' arc minutes. In both instruments, the graduation scale chosen for the quadrants is finer than was necessary for the context.

Now it may be objected that the large Samrat Yantra was designed not only to observe the sun but also to measure the path of the stars, and because of its relatively small diameter, a star can be observed more accurately. But the large Samrat Yantras were also too large for this purpose, because contemporary sighting methods using a string or a sighting tube – only usable for instruments on the scale of the Rashi Valaya Yantras – made it impossible to take advantage of the extremely fine subdivision of the scales. It seems surprising that Jai Singh should channel the energy of his collaborators into building ever larger instruments rather than improving the most simple observation instruments, especially since alidades, used for centuries in Arabian observatories, could not have been totally unknown to him. In fact, he seems to have taken relatively little interest in perfecting his instruments, as he had already completed his astronomical tables by 1728 with the aid of just a few stone and small metal instruments, before the four other observatories had either been completed or even planned. His collection of precisely made traditional metal instruments also suggests that he had no need of the enormous yantras for the purposes of observation.[71]

The idea that Jai Singh's instruments were both pointless and unnecessary is not new. A few decades after the maharaja's death, J. L. Williams in Benares received some information which pointed in this direction. In a letter to W. Marsden he writes:

70 *Zig Mohammad Shahi*, translated into English by William Hunter, see 'Some Accounts of the Astronomical Labours of Jayasinha', in *Asiatic Researches*, vol. 5, 1799.

71 Some small metal instruments are to be found in the palace museum. James Tod writes that one of Jai Singh's successors had most of them melted down or sold them; see note 76.

An account of the use of the different instruments, though very imperfect, was given me on the spot, by several learned Brahmins who attended me; one of whom is professor of astronomy in the new founded college at Benares. They all agreed that this observatory never was used, nor did they think it capable of being used, for any nice observations; and believe that it was built more for ostentation, than the promotion of useful knowledge.[72]

This damning judgement about the scientific uses of Jai Singh's astronomical instruments may have gone a little too far, but it is not totally unjustified. Let us recall that the yantras in Jaipur, Delhi, Benares and Ujjain vary a great deal in size. What did Jai Singh hope to achieve, for example, by building a smaller Samrat Yantra in Benares after already building a much larger one in Delhi? Jagannath's explanation that the point of the observatory in Benares was to check[73] the readings obtained in Delhi is rendered implausible by the difference in size – unless one presumes that it had also become clear to Jai Singh that there was no advantage in making very large instruments. But then the building of the observatories would certainly have been pointless.

It seems clear, then, that Jai Singh's constructions were not used for astronomical readings to the extent which the precisely made measuring scales suggest.

Jai Singh had European advisers at his court for many years. First of all there were the Jesuits who advised the maharaja in questions of astronomy and mathematics and in so doing earned the right to build a church and to continue their missionary work undisturbed.

On the advice of Father Emmanuel de Figueredo, to whom Jai Singh was indebted for technical information, the maharaja sent a legation to Lisbon, led by de Figueredo himself. He returned in 1729[74] armed with all the latest knowledge about astronomical discoveries. In

1734, he was succeeded by the French Jesuits Pons and Boudier[75] and finally by a series of German priests. They were all knowledgeable about astronomy and must have told Jai Singh about the way contemporary European observatories were being built. But the maharaja obviously showed no interest in alidades and telescopes, which at this time were the standard equipment of every observatory; nor did the fact that the European astronomical tables – drawn up with the aid of small instruments and not inferior to his own – deter him from his plan to build large and expensive observatories in stone. Wherever the Mogul emperor installed him as governor of a province, he built yantras which could be seen from a great distance.

In view of the enormous building costs and the modest scientific value of Jai Singh's works, it seems reasonable to assume that this was a case of a headstrong monarch looking to construct huge and extravagant monuments for himself. Observations in his five observatories produced no new results. His main work, *Zig Muhammad Shahi*, the tables dedicated to the Mogul emperor, are essentially based on Ulugh Beg's tables and on European sources. The name Jai Singh is therefore only rarely mentioned in the history of astronomy. His buildings up until now have only been regarded as a curiosity and only a single astronomer, Kaye, thought it worthwhile to undertake a precise analysis of Jai Singh's works at the beginning of the 20th century.[76]

From a functional point of view, an examination of Jai Singh's instruments proves to be relatively unrewarding, since it fails to confirm that their form was based on their function. Consequently, an analysis of their capabilities as astronomical instruments sheds little light on them as architecture.

There are, however, indications which suggest a different interpretation of Jai Singh's building activities, one which may not immediately occur to the Western-oriented architectural critic accustomed to certain conceptual

72 'Further Particulars Respecting the Observatory at Benares', *Philosophical Transactions of the Royal Society of London,* MDCCXCIII, part 1, letter of 31 January 1793, p. 45ff.

73 *Zig Mohammad Shahi*, translated into English by William Hunter, see 'Some Accounts of the Astronomical Labours of Jayasinha', in Asiatic Researches, vol. 5, 1799.

74 According to S. Noti, *Land und Volk des königlichen Astronomer Dschaisingh, II. Maharadscha von Dschaipur,* Berlin, 1911, p. 91.

75 See *Lettres Edifiantes,* vol. 15, no. 33.

76 Only a few items have survived, as S. Noti explains, 'Bad times were to descend upon Jaipur under the fourth successor of Jai Singh, the degenerate Jagat Singh II (1803–1818) …After Jagat Singh had emptied the rich national treasury to satisfy the capricious whims of his Muslim concubine, Ras-Kaphar, it was the turn of the treasures in the valuable library and the metal instruments of the observatory. The books and manuscripts were sold off by the hundredweight as wrapping paper to the shopkeepers of the town and surrounding area; whilst the brass fittings of the huge gnomons and the metal instruments, small or large, were traded in to local and foreign coppersmiths.'

categories. However, by fitting together various pieces of circumstantial evidence which at first sight have no obvious connection with Jai Singh's observatories, this new interpretation is unavoidable.

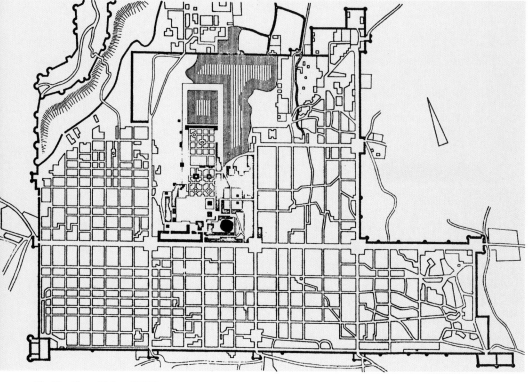

Fig. 99   Plan of Jaipur (1727).

The Town of Jaipur

The instruments built during Jai Singh's lifetime were designed by the Raj Guru Jagannath [77] and Guru Vidyadhar. [78] They were both members of the priest cast and the title 'guru' broadly speaking means 'spiritual adviser'. In this capacity, Vidyadhar also designed the town plan of Jaipur. He not only played the role of priest, but was also a 'sthapati', a Hindu priest-architect.

According to the ancient Indian sacred architectural manuals, every building project has its symbolic cosmological aspect. The design's conformity to natural laws and the rites surrounding

its construction were known only to the *sthapati*. Before building got under way, he established all the dimensions, and planned out the work and the ceremonies. [79] Buildings which did not conform to these plans brought misfortune to the architect and to the occupant. [80]

Could Jaipur still have been permeated with these old traditions in the 18th century? Or is the town on the contrary an early experiment in planning streets and houses in India according to a logical pattern, with uniform blocks of houses and a rectangular street plan? Is the street plan analogous to the grid-like plan adopted in 19th-century European and American towns for commercial reasons. Or does Jaipur have more in common with the Roman castrum, or even ancient Indian and Chinese geomantic town planning?

In numerous publications, the town of Jaipur was acclaimed by European academics as an early triumph of rational logic over the attitudes and behaviour of the local Hindu people, who were steeped in the traditions of magic and myth. In so doing they made the same mistake as people today who see Jai Singh's yantras as the work of a sort of proto-Cubist. [81] The latter, like the former, are judging the town and the individual buildings by criteria which were of no concern to the ruler, architect or priest in 18th-century India. For them, the founding of a town was a ritual. The Brahman Vidyadhar saw Jaipur as a golden opportunity to plan a whole town according to the principles of Hindu architectural theory. Almost all Indian towns at this time presented a chaotic picture of narrow twisting lanes, a confusion of run-down palaces and temporary shacks. These shapeless conglomerations of buildings had arisen from the haphazard growth of village settlements and a timid adherence to tradition had prevented any change in design. But towns like this bore no relation at all to the principles set out in Hindu architectural manuals, which call for strict geometrical planning. [82] More often than not a square or rectan-

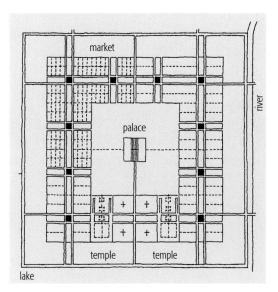

Fig. 100   Plan of Hangzhou in China, 13th century, as it was in descriptions by Marco Polo.

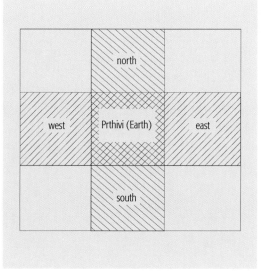

Fig. 101   In the pithapada mandala the earth is located in the centre square normally reserved for Brahma.

77 According to Gokul Chandra Bhawan.
78 'Vidhyadhur, one of his chief coadjutators in his astronomical pursuits, and whose genius planned the city of Jeipoor, was a Jain, and claimed spiritual descent from the celebrated Hemacharya, of Nehvalla, minister and spiritual guide of his namesake, the great Jey Sing (1094–1145)', James Tod, *Annals and Antiquities of Rajasthan,* vol. 2, London, 1832, p. 367.
79 See the author's *Living architecture: Indian,* New York and London, 1969; and D. N. Shukla, *Vastu-Sastra.* vol. 1, *Hindu Science of Architecture,* Delhi, 1995.
80 See N. K. Bose, *Orissan Architecture,* Calcutta, 1931.
81 For example, P. Chetwode, 'Delhi Observatory, The Paradise of an Early Cubist', *The Architectural Review,* 1935.
82 See, for example, Prasanna Kumar Acharya, *An Encyclopedia of Hindu Architecture,* Oxford University Press, 1927–46.
83 See Stella Kramrisch, *The Hindu Temple,* 2 vols., University of Calcutta, 1946.
84 See D. N. Shukla, *Vastu-Sastra.* vol. 1, *Hindu Science of Architecture,* Delhi, 1995.
85 See Stella Kramrisch, *The Hindu Temple,* 2 vols., University of Calcutta, 1946.
86 Ibid.; mandalas with 4×4 square fields, for example, have no square in the middle.

gular representation of the world, a so-called mandala, is recommended as a basis for the plan, the overall composition of which is divided into separate fields. Each field, called a *pada,* is the seat of a deity.[83]

The town plan of Jaipur is primarily divided into 3×3 *padas.* Unusually, the central field, which is normally assigned to Brahma, the highest god, is not occupied by a temple dedicated to Brahma but by the secular palace of the maharaja. This contradicted the guidelines found in many of the old manuals according to which the king was entitled to the *padas* in the east of the town but not to that most sacred of places, the centre, which is reserved for the temple.[84] This contradiction can be explained, however, if we compare the mandala of Jaipur with a nine-part mandala described by Stella Kramrisch, the pithapada.[85]

In the third type of plan, the Pithapada of nine squares, the central square is occupied by Prthivi, and the four Vedas should be worshipped in the four directions surrounded on all sides by the respective deities. This plan is an amplified Prthivi-mandala; besides, in its construction it is parallel to those of the plan of a higher order. Here it is Prthivi, the Earth, who holds the central square – 'the measure is this terrestrial world (S.B. VIII.3.3.5.) and not Brahma, the Supreme Principle. In this, the Pithapada is unique among those plans (mandalas), which have a central plot.'[86]

Not only does this quotation from the *Brhat Samhita* perhaps unravel the mystery of the town plan of Jaipur, it also shows that the *Brhat Samhita* must have been known to the architect and guru Vidyadhar and that he undoubtedly belonged to the tradition of the Hindu priest-architects, the *sthapatis,* who were familiar with the strictly guarded secrets of how the mandala was produced. He was able to comply with Jai Singh's understandable desire for a palace in the centre of the new town of Jaipur because out of the large number of town-plan mandalas to choose from, he picked the only one with the Earth at its centre instead of Brahma. As ruler over the immanent world, Jai Singh was perfectly

Fig. 102 A Tibetan mandala used when preparing for meditation.

entitled to the centre of the town in a town built in accordance with the pithapada mandala.[87]

Moreover, the ground plan of the palace and the street plan of the surrounding town (fig. 99), or rather the mandala it is based on, are turned at an angle of 12° from the principal compass points. This is also no coincidence, for the plan is oriented on the star sign Leo instead of to the north, and Leo is the zodiacal sign of the Kacchwaha dynasty, i.e. Jai Singh's family.

Today, no town in India points more clearly to the mandala symbolism and to astrological references than Jaipur. The only irregularity is the tenth district, which was added on to the square town plan in the south-east, but this was a later alterations to the town.

The theory of the mandala as a graphic aid to knowledge is not confined to Hinduism and Buddhism. C. G. Jung paid special attention to it, collecting a large number of geometrical drawings from his patients which are similar to the square or circular Indian mandalas. Among his comments on the subject we find the following:

> Unity and wholeness stand at the top of the objective scale of values for their symbols can no longer be distinguished from the imago Dei. And so all statements about the image of God automatically hold good for the empirical symbols of wholeness. Experience shows that the individual mandalas are symbols of order, thus they arise in patients mainly during times of psychic disorientation or reorientation. In the same way as a magic circle, they banish and exorcize the lawless powers of darkness and illustrate an order or generate such an order which changes chaos into a cosmos.[88]

This statement by a psychiatrist coincides exactly with the comments found in many Hindu architectural manuals regarding the significance of mandalas. Jung points to the fact that even

87 The correspondences demonstrated by the author in his *Living Architecture: Indian*, New York and London, 1969, between the ground plans of temples and the descriptions of the mandalas translated by Kramrisch no longer leave any doubt about the reliability of such comparisons.

88 Carl Gustav Jung, *Configurations of the Unconscious*, in *Collected Works of C. G. Jung*, vol. 18, Princeton University Press, 1977.

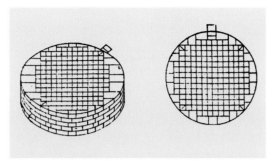

Fig. 103   The stone blocks in the bases of the Rama Yantras in Jaipur are arranged in a similar fashion to the bricks in the Vedic fire altar.

in the Middle Ages in Europe a large number of mandala signs are detectable, above all the specifically Christian form in the representation of Christ and the symbols of the evangelists in the four compass points:

> Later there is a small, extremely interesting mandala in Jakob Boehme's book about the soul. It is absolutely obvious there that it is a psychocosmic system with a strong Christian element. It is called the 'philosophical eye' or the 'mirror of wisdom', by which a summa of the secret knowledge is obviously meant. More often than not it is in the shape of a flower, cross or wheel with a clear preference for the number four (reminiscent of the Pythagorean tetractys, the cardinal number). Mandalas such as this can also be found as sand drawings used by the Pueblos for ritual purposes. [89]

There are several possible ways of representing a mandala in India. It can be drawn, it can be danced and it can dictate the structure of a building [90] or a sculpture. [91] In the context of Jai Singh's architecture, it is not only the mandalas on which the town plan is based which are of interest but also those which can be seen in the foundations of individual buildings. A feature of almost all Hindu temples is that they are built on a platform consisting of a raised slab foundation. The size of the platform is predetermined by the mandala chosen by the priest-architect. Slab foundations of this kind are unknown to Islamic architects. In Islamic domestic and sacred buildings, the walls are usually built on strip foundations. These strip foundations are calculated from figures drawn from past experience and are not visible when looking at the building. Platform-type foundations are therefore only found where Hindus, for theological reasons, need a horizontal level for the ritual of producing the mandala.

A large proportion of the instruments constructed by Jai Singh and his successors are based on Hindu tradition. In addition to the instruments in Ujjain, the following are built on platforms:

1) the Dakshino Bhitti Yantra in Jaipur with a rectangular platform built of limestone,
2) the small and the large Rama Yantras of Jaipur with a circular platform,
3) the Rashi Valaya Yantras in Jaipur which have a common platform,
4) the Small Samrat Yantra in Jaipur,
5) the house of the astronomer in Jaipur with a square platform,
6) the Great Samrat Yantra in Benares.

Now the objection may be made that a horizontal plane was necessary for calculating certain points on the scales when each instrument was being built. This function alone does not explain the emphasis on these, however.

What connections do the foundations of a yantra in Jaipur or Benares have with the Hindu mandala? Before this question can be adequately answered, we need to examine more closely the origin of the slab foundation and the mandala.

The process of producing order with the aid of graphics, which led to the development of the platform, can be traced back to the Vedic period. The precursor of the slab foundation under buildings is the Vedic fire altar.

89 Carl Gustav Jung, *Commentary on the 'Secret of the Golden Flower'*, Collected Works of C. G. Jung, vol. 13, Princeton University Press, 1967.
90 See Dharmaraja Ratha, on p. 138 of the author's *Living Architecture: Indian*, New York and London, 1969.
91 Detailed representation in Alice Boner, *Principles of Composition in Hindu Sculpture*, Leiden, 1962.

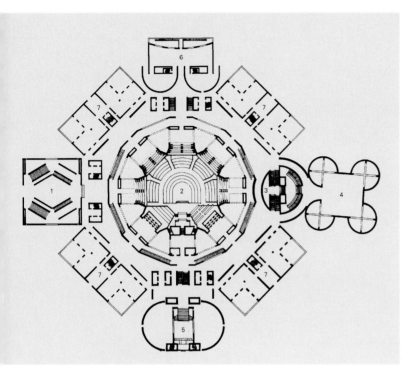

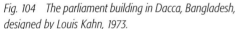

Fig. 104   The parliament building in Dacca, Bangladesh, designed by Louis Kahn, 1973.

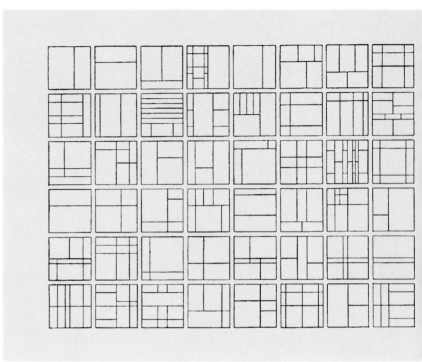

Fig. 105   Le Corbusier's 'Game of Filling in a Square', based on his proportional system, the 'Modulor', 1949.

The place of the flame is now taken by the structure of its [the temple's] socle; it arises with perpendicular walls and a pointed superstructure. Neither the form of the socle with its horizontal mouldings nor that of the temple on it imply a derivation from the form of the Agni (fire altar) or its flame; but it is the knowledge of these rites which survives in architectural form. Even in some of the last buildings in which a living tradition was at work . . . the memory survives of the substance of which the altar was built; wherein had been placed the heads of the sacrificial victims, man, horse and other 'animals'.[92]

Kramrisch only applies this interpretation of the temple platform based on old manuscripts to buildings built before the 13th century. But the temples built during the next six centuries demonstrate that the importance of the platform

as an altar has been well known to Hindu architects right up until the present. The presumption of many historians that a wide gap in knowledge separates the architects of the newer temples from the old architectural theorists would appear to be supported by the inferior artistic quality of the new buildings, but appearances are deceptive here. The author had the opportunity to see in Alice Boner's[93] and Pundit Sadasiva Rath Sarma's library in Benares a large number of unpublished manuscripts on architectural theory from different centuries. These manuscripts suggest that Hindu architectural theory did not sink into oblivion while the Muslim sultans and moguls were ruling the Indian subcontinent.

Mandala theory, like the tradition of the slab foundations, can also be traced back to the Vedic altar. If one presupposes an uninterrupted building tradition, then the only visible stone site of a slab foundation in Jaipur, that of the Great Rama Yantra (see fig. 95), recalls the Vedic altar

92 Stella Kramrisch, *The Hindu Temple,* 2 vols., University of Calcutta, 1946, p. 146; the *Brhat Samhita* was the source.
93 See A. Boner and S. Rath Sarma, *Silpa Prakasa,* Leiden, 1966.
94 P. K. Acharya, *An Encyclopedia of Hindu Architecture,* Oxford University Press, 1927–46.
95 Vitruvius, *De Architectura,* translated by Joseph Gwilt, London, 1826.

Fig. 106 An early sketch by Le Corbusier for the roof shap of the parliament building in Chandigarh. He borrowed shapes from Jai Singh's buildings.

and its precisely prescribed stone or brick bond.

What could have induced the architects of the Rama Yantras in Jaipur to build up the quadrants of the slab foundations in a strictly geometrical fashion? There was no visual reason for doing so, because this geometrical division is concealed by the stone supports which rest on it and are constructed quite independently of it. There is also no technical reason for it, since to make this pattern they had to cut the blocks specially in the same width when it would have been much simpler to fit them together irregularly, as can be seen, for example, in many of the Rashi Valaya Yantras.

We are not claiming that the slab foundations of the Rama Yantras are direct copies of a Vedic fire altar or even altar themelves! We are merely pointing out that certain architectural and symbolic forms demonstrably run through Hindu architecture right down to the present day.

Fig. 107 The parliament building in Chandigarh, designed by Le Corbusier, 1957–59.

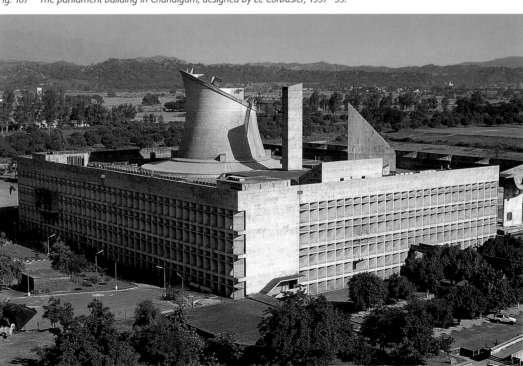

Such similarities are of course also the result of unchanged construction methods. A fire altar was built in the following way: at the equinox, east-west was established with the help of a gnomon using the method which is described in the Manasara manuscript[94] (and also by Vitruvius).[95] The first row of stones was laid out from east to west and north-south was obtained from its perpendicular.

Looking at the stone layout of the foundation slab, it is immediately apparent that the architects of the Rama Yantra followed this tradition. A continuous row of stones running exactly from east to west and a row of slabs laid from north to south in the second stage of work form the basic framework of the round stone surface. Before building up the quadrants in a herringbone pattern, they established the circumference of the circle in the third stage and constructed the circular boundary wall. The ancient Indian model can also be recognized in this process.

The most important initial steps in building a Rama Yantra, namely establishing the east-west and the north-south axes and the circumference, can again be detected in the large low platform in Jaipur known as 'Jai Singh's Seat' (fig. 86). Is this procedure not reminiscent of the 'orientatio' and 'limitatio' in Roman settlements?[96] Are we not looking in both cases at those same psychocosmograms which C. G. Jung describes as symbols of wholeness?

These are the quaternity and mandala symbols which occur not only in the dreams of unsuspecting modern man but are also widespread in ancient monuments of many races and ages. Their meaning as symbols of unity and wholeness is sufficiently substantiated historically as well as empirically and psychologically.[97]

If we look for those kinds of 'forms of the unconscious'[98] in architecture since Ledoux, we will find no greater master of transferring symbolic shapes into architectural shapes than the American architect Louis Kahn. We can see the sharp contrast between his formal language and the 'forms of the conscious' of Le Corbusier, who in fact even in his game of filling in a square in the 'Modulor'[99] is not afraid of producing quite grotesque-looking efforts to deliberately avoid the quaternity symbol.

Yet we are told by Le Corbusier himself that every time he went to Chandigarh he stopped off in Delhi and went into the Jantar Mantar observatory, where he occasionally sketched. He was less fascinated by the function or the symbolism of the yantras than the way they play with pure geometrical shapes. He did not copy the instruments exactly – as can be seen from the way he placed a structure similar in form to one of the cooling towers in Ahmedabad on the parliament building of Chandigarh. The silhouette of this building, for example, contains a few 'pseudo-astronomical' forms imitating the observatories, forms like the pyramid pointing up to the sky, the diagonally-cut roof in the style of the sundials (Narivalaya Uttar Gola, Kranti Writta) and the vaulted canopy, the side view of which is reminiscent of the quadrants of the Samrat Yantras (fig. 107).

The Mandala as a Yantra

Jai Singh's instruments were always called 'yantras', and the overall concept of the yantra is linked to the mandala. The essential characteristic of mandalas is that they *illustrate* and in so doing become aids to knowledge. Created as a projection or vision in a person's thoughts, they transmit in a visual form characteristic identification marks, but have no effect on their surroundings other than to communicate a sign.

The crucial step from the mandala to the yantra is that the mandala acquires a *psychic*

96 Inauguratio, limitatio, orientatio and consecratio were adopted by the Etruscans.
97 Carl Gustav Jung, Aion, in Collected Works of C. G. Jung, vol. 9, Princeton University Press, 1969, p. 55.
98 To paraphrase Jung's title, Configurations of the Unconscious.
99 Le Corbusier, Le Modulor, Modulor 2, English edition, Birkhauser, 2000.

Fig. 108   Drawing of a Tantric sculpture based on a yantra, c. 12th century.

100   Alice Boner, *Principles of Composition in Hindu
Sculpture,* Leiden, 1962.

effect. Only through this effect or power does the
sign or symbol change into a 'yantra', which
means 'instrument'. This aspect of a mandala was
of much greater importance for Hindu theologians and *sthapatis* than comparable symbols of
wholeness for the mystics of other cultures.

Alongside the esoteric meaning of the concept
of a yantra, in Tantric teaching it can also be used
for an instrument in the sense of a tool or a
mechanism. Only the context makes it possible
to determine whether a saw or a hammer or a
symbolic figure such as a mandala, for example,
is meant. This difference is unimportant, since
the yantra as a 'device' does not presuppose a
clear, one-sided physically or clearly defined
metaphysical purpose.

The yantra theory finds expression in Indian
architecture whenever the conformity to a law of
a transcendent reality is to be demonstrated and
manifested by the representation of a mandala,
and whenever the power, which only the initi-
ated person understands how to use, is ascribed
to the representation. In the priest's hands, the
yantra as crystallised truth becomes a means of
determining the fates of fellow human beings,
and even of the gods themselves. This aspect of
yantras obviously creates a need for secrecy.

The mandala on the foundation slab of a temple is not the only geometric figure of a building
which is used as a yantra. All Tantric sculptures
are based on a yantra,[100] and according to recent
research all the art and architecture of the Indian
subcontinent appears to be permeated with
Tantric theories. The essential element of a
sculpture or building then is not its form but the
yantra giving rise to it. Buildings were covered
with rich formal decoration and fascinating
pictorial content by the architects and sculptors
(such as the depiction of erotic scenes in
Khajuraho or Konarak) so that the uninitiated
would not experience any of the magic power.

What have the Tantric yantras in common
with Jai Singh's instruments apart from the
name? The architects were priests and mystics

and the foundation slabs of the Rama Yantras are made according to an ancient rite. Most of the buildings are useless for accurate readings and the same types of buildings are repeated unnecessarily. The yantra, the geomantic tool and key to the most secret knowledge, represents the culmination of Indian mandala theory. There thus appears to be only one single interpretation possible for Jai Singh's buildings: his yantras are representations of the world and of contemporary cosmology; or, in the words of Father Strobl, every yantra is a 'machine representing perpetual motion'.[101]

For centuries Hindu priests had endeavoured to design an image of the universe with the seats of the gods and the realms of humans. The man who knew the geometric key to the world was sure of possessing worldly and spiritual power. In Jai Singh's day, the influence of Islam and Christianity was leading people to doubt the validity of the old magic squares. Consequently, it may have been the prince's greatest ambition to create an up-to-date portrayal of the universe, a representation of the geometric relationships between earth, sun, stars and planets. This would not only have been a demonstration of his knowledge, but also of the power which, according to the old teachings, he exercised over his fellow human beings through this knowledge.

An analysis of the possible theological, geomantic and scientific prerequisites which enabled Jai Singh's instruments to be built to a large extent disregards the theoretical considerations accompanying every formal process. But every construction, and indeed every one of its details, mirrored a whole maze of decisions concerning architectural theory for which even the Indian *sthapati* had to render account, unless he could unthinkingly bring in to play a rigid formal canon and a theory of proportion sanctified by tradition as a solution to an everyday task.

The building of an observatory was not an everyday task and there were no tried and tested models. Every line, every dimension and every

composition had to be thought through. The similar shapes of the instruments in different towns show that those who designed them not only worked to an overall concept but also had an idea of the solutions to details, extending right up to the completion of the building.

That the work was carried out by Jai Singh and his fellow workers in so few years and executed on such a breathtakingly monumental scale is an admirable achievement. It would have required a team of workmen and artists skilled in traditional techniques who were bursting with cosmological and architectural ideas, so that it only needed an initial spark of enthusiasm from a keen patron for a concept developed and refined over centuries to find expression in a physical form.

It is impossible to reconstruct the process involved, since we only have the end product to draw on. Also, the thought processes of Jai Singh's architects would probably not be comprehensible to us since we – as they were – are trapped in an outlook loaded with axioms from a particular age. Nevertheless, let us attempt to discover some kind of structure in Jai Singh's architecture using some of the criteria taken from present-day architectural theory. The weakness of this inevitably fragmentary way of looking at things is that it does not take into account the complexities and contradictions of an all-embracing world view such as that held by present-day architectural specialists and thus can only yield statements which may be correct, but are unhelpful.

The Ground Plan

For each group of buildings constructed at the same time, is there a general rule which governs the spatial relationship between the buildings? In Delhi, Jaipur, Benares or Ujjain, we would

101 R. P. A. Strobl, *Brieffe aus Ost-Indien*, in *Allerhand so Lehr- als Geistreiche Brieffe, Schriften…*, edited by F. Keller, Vienna, 1758, no. 644, p. 15.

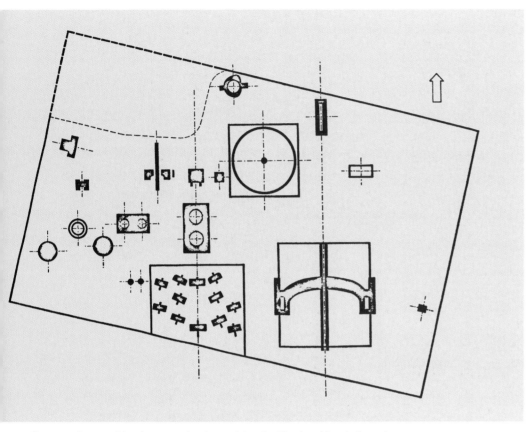

Fig. 109   Diagram of the observatory in Jaipur as it is today. The dotted lines indicate the axes.

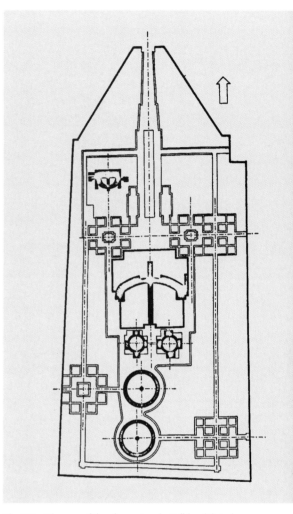

Fig. 110   Diagram of the observatory in Delhi as it is today. The dotted lines indicate the axes.

expect to find a pattern having its roots in numerology or cosmological symbolism, possibly also an axial construction that might have been adapted from late Mogul architecture.

A numerical connection, which could have been easy to establish once the contemporary measuring system was known,[102] cannot be detected in any of the observatories. Furthermore, a classification according to geometrical rules would have come to light after the measurements taken by the author in 1966 and 1967 in Delhi, Jaipur, Benares and Ujjain, since the rules of proportion in Indian architecture are widely known and the ground plans were studied for just such

a possibility. The search for axial links, however, has been more fruitful. In Jaipur, the Narivalaya Uttar Gola, Jai Prakash Yantras and Rashi Valaya Yantras share a common axis, likewise the Great Samrat Yantra and the Dakshino Bhitti Yantra. In Delhi, the garden grounds are clearly axially situated in relation to the instruments.

If one takes into account the historical development of these two observatories, though, then out of all the axes there is only one which falls in Jai Singh's time. It is the first one, the north-south axis, which extends from the Rashi Valaya Yantras. The Dakshino Bhitti Yantra was not put in its present-day position in the north-

102 The author reconstructed all units of measurement used for the buildings and models.

103 According to A. Garrett and Ch. Guleri, *The Jaipur Observatory and its Builder,* Allahabad, 1902.

104 Kaye did not locate them during his 1915–16 visit.

105 See quotation 72 on p. 103.

106 K. A. Doxiadis, *Raumordnung im griechischen Städtebau,* Berlin, 1937.

107 For the reasoning, see pp. 78–82.

108 Edmund Bacon, *Design of Cities,* London, 1967.

ern extension of the axis of the Samrat Yantra until 1876,[103] and the grounds in Delhi are modern,[104] although they are laid out in the style of a Mogul garden. It is thus not possible to speak in general terms of an axis system in Jai Singh's architecture.

The observatories were above all conceived as magnificent monuments. Local scholars in Benares[105] emphasized this a few years after Jai Singh's death. Is it not therefore possible that the architects chose the position and size of the individual instruments so as to achieve the most impressive stage set possible, creating an overall effect of perspective in the same way as the master builders of the Renaissance and the Baroque strove to do in the West? The difficulty of finding a good position for an overall view in any of the observatories shows that Jai Singh's architects did not intend anything of the sort. If you want to photograph several of the yantras together, for example, then you have to choose a high vantage point since at eye level there is rarely any kind of staggered arrangement or studied composition. Jai Singh's architects cannot have had any carefully thought-out visual effect in mind, such as the one K. Doxiadis[106] outlines for a person

walking through the Propylaea in Athens. There is no centre and no main focal point. The instruments do not in any way interact with or influence the site, which in Jaipur has not even been levelled off. The only order lies in their common orientation on the celestial pole. Each individual building, however, forms a harmonious whole in its own right, set off against the surrounding instruments by its own individual shape and referring only to itself through its symmetrical construction – even where this has no function, as in the Mishra Yantra.[107]

We come across a similar phenomenon in the town plan of ancient Rome. The monumental buildings which towered above the monotonous mass of houses – theatres, bath-houses, stadia and palaces – are built strictly axially but stand completely unrelated to each other. What Edmund N. Bacon wrote about ancient Rome could be applied to the ground plans of Jai Singh's observatories:

The whole design was held together by the sheer mass of its individual elements, each bound to another by the friction of compression caused by the ever-growing city.[108]

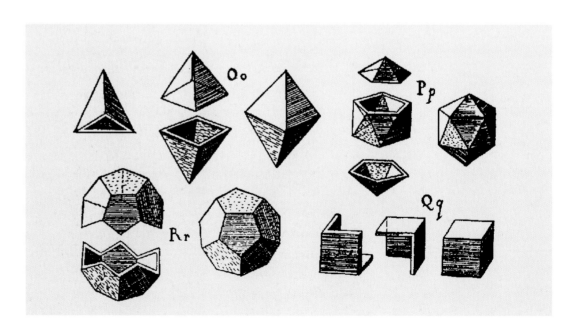

Fig. 111   The five regular bodies which Kepler used to discover the architecture of the universe. They were first mentioned by Pythagoras, and are also known as Pythagorean bodies.

Fig. 112   Design for the Cenotaph of Newton by Etienne-Louis Boullée.

In Rome, as in Jaipur and Delhi, the architects had come to the same conclusion in their deliberations about the purpose of axiality: it can make good sense to join individual parts of a formal total structure together by means of axes. Placing closed in, autonomous structures such as an amphitheatre or a Rama Yantra in proximity to other autonomous structures, however, suggests an intention to play down their intrinsic value, leading ultimately to rivalling effects cancelling each other out. Moreover, wherever this experiment was put into practice in town planning the architecture became frozen in an unconvincing formalism.

The Individual Building

In Hindu monumental architecture, we rarely encounter buildings whose function is primarily spatial. Many Hindu monumental buildings lack interior space of any consequence, but their solid mass relates to, and influences, the surrounding space. These different spatial concepts can be compared to a hollow sphere which, from the inside, appears only as a spatial limitation without any solid substance but, seen from outside, appears merely as a three-dimensional body lacking any function of spatial limitation.

Jai Singh's yantras belong to that category of solid buildings which do not enclose anything.

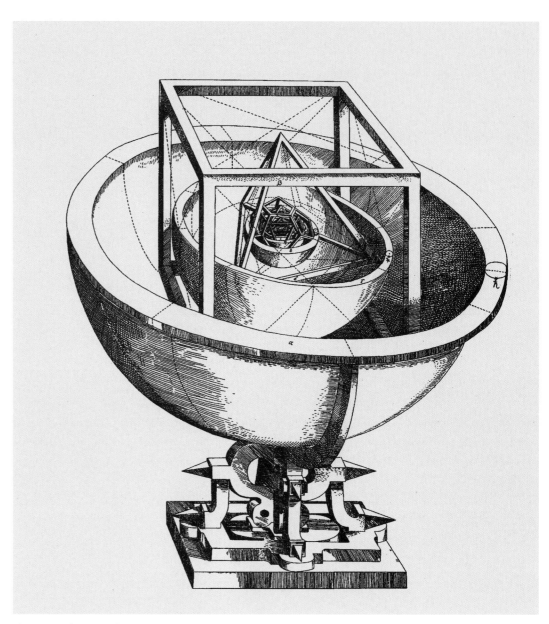

Fig. 113   Kepler's Mysterium Cosmographicum.

This was an inevitable consequence of their function, since the buildings with their instruments had to face the sky. They thus corresponded exactly to the Hindu ideal of architecture as solid mass. This was quite possibly why fewer pilot schemes were needed before the architects were able to find forms for these stone-built instruments which are still convincing today. In the West, architects think in two or three projection planes. In sacred buildings, for instance, a special symbolic meaning is ascribed to the ground plan. Consequently, views of the ceiling or spatial diagrams, as Bruno Zevi suggests, are important for understanding architectural form.[109]

At the same time as Baroque architects were taking the use of interior space to new heights, Indian *sthapatis* were building the yantras of the observatories which, like Hindu temples, are exclusively oriented outwards. They can only be portrayed incompletely in projection planes, since neither a horizontal nor a vertical section can record this outwards-oriented shape. The most important surface on this type of building is the top. For that reason, in the Small Samrat Yantra of Jaipur it was emphasized by using a uniform design in white stone on horizontal surfaces.

In the temple cities of the Hindus or Jains, whose buildings point towards the sky for theological rather than astronomical reasons, the observer can rarely find a high viewpoint which makes a top view possible. In the observatories, the large number of staircases usually permits a view from the higher instruments down on to the lower ones, giving a better idea of the spatial disposition of the yantras (fig. 58).

Let us consider the shape of the buildings again. The smooth flat stonework is not typical of either Hindu or Islamic buildings. Comparisons with Cubism are also misleading.[111] The geometrical construction of the various parts is anchored in the idea of a geometrically defined cosmos. The ancient Indian cosmological ideas of the world mountain Meru had lost their influence and the Copernican conception of the world had not yet been fully accepted.[112]

The astronomers found themselves in a situation which is comparable to that of the young Kepler in that between the new scientific and the old theological interpretation of the cosmos there was in each case a period of geometrical and numerological speculation. From Jai Singh's day, only the yantras bear witness to that, but from Kepler we have the *Mysterium cosmographicum* and the *Harmonice mundi*. In these works, Kepler drew and described what Jai Singh constructed in stone: a cosmos created according to geometrical principles, whose harmony man was trying to understand, whether in the image of the 'mystery of the cosmos' or the yantra.

Here we see how God, like a human architect, according to order and principle, has approached the laying of the foundations of the world and has measured everything in such a way that one would like to think it was not art which was taking nature as its model but that in creation God himself looked at the building methods of future generations. (Johannes Kepler, *Mysterium cosmographicum*)

In many respects, the architecture of a contemporary of Jai Singh II, Étienne-Louis Boullée (1728–1799), has a comparable link with cosmology. The most striking of Boullée's works in this respect are the Newton Cenotaph, which is in the form of an enormous sphere with the starry sky projected on its inner surface, and his ground plan for a national palace in the shape of a mandala.

There are several parallels between the designs of Boullée and Jai Singh, notably their huge, monumental dimensions, their explicit cosmological connections and, as C.G. Jung might have put it, their clear preference for symbols of wholeness which, in the case of quaternity or mandala symbols, spring from the collective unconscious.

Oh Newton! If you have defined the shape of the earth through the extent of your knowledge and your awe-inspiring genius then I have designed the plan to cloak you in your discovery, to cloak you in yourself as it were. But how is it possible to find something outside your Self where nothing can exist which is worthy of you![113]

All the examples of cosmological architecture highlight man's need to bring his existence and his knowledge into a correspondence with the form of the universe, which is so difficult to describe. Jai Singh thus follows a succession of architects and artists who took up the same challenge in quite different cultural contexts, projecting an image of the universe and its laws appropriate to their own time.

109 Bruno Zevi, *Saper vedere l'architettura*, Milan, 1948.
110 See also note 30.
111 See cover picture of the *Lexikon der Modernen Baukunst*, Knaur, 1966.
112 The astronomical concepts of Jai Singh are described in detail in G. R. Kaye, *The Astronomical Observatories of Jai Singh*, Calcutta, 1918.
113 Quotation after Philippe Madec, *Etienne-Louis Boullée*, Basel, Boston and Berlin, 1989, p. 63.

4 | Architectural Models

There is no suggestion in contemporary sources or later descriptions of Jai Singh's observatories that the construction of any of the instruments was preceded by pilot studies or preparatory architectural models. On the whole, we know very little about contemporary design methods. Did they draw ground plans and elevations for the structures? Or did they, as local architects had been doing for centuries, only establish the most important measurements, the proportions and geometrical relations, and then leave the shaping of particular details to the craftsmen making them? Although it would be reasonable to suppose that they adopted the latter approach, which was the typical Hindu way (after all, it was only Hindu *sthapatis* and craftsmen who were involved in the building), this is actually unlikely because it presupposes an old building tradition in which each craftsman was familiar with details used many times before, as well as with the overall shape.

There were no models in India for the yantras in the observatories. None of the architects and craftsmen were able to use familiar shapes. They had to construct buildings with unfamiliar forms, full of complicated geometrical requirements, something which would have been almost impossible without two-dimensional representations. Unfortunately no such plans have survived, but there are a series of models which, amazingly, were never publicized, although they sometimes surpass the buildings in both their form and the beauty of the materials used. Some of these architectural models are in the safe keeping of the Brahman

Fig. 114 Wooden model of the Samrat Yantra in Jaipur.

who is the present-day guardian of the observatory in Jaipur; some only came to light underneath rubble during clearance work by the author on the ground floor of the Dakshino Bhitti.[114] The exact dates for these models are not known, but comparison with the building, an inscription or the workmanship sometimes suggest a date. The majority are certainly older than the group of models which, according to information provided by T. H. Hendley, were made at the end of the 19th century and are now in the Science Museum in London (these more recent models are not discussed in this chapter, but illustrations of them appear on pages 49 and 57).

Model of the Great Samrat Yantra (fig. 114)

There is a precisely crafted wooden model of the Great Samrat Yantra in the grounds of the observatory. It stands in one of the keel-arched niches in the perimeter wall of the courtyard. This model differs from the building in its present-day form in only a few details. For example, it shows the keel arches set in the meridian wall as being more evenly spaced. The later walling up or reduction in size of the openings of the arches was presumably done to reinforce the wall.

In the original version of the model, the wall surfaces were painted yellow. The intrados of the arches, however, were white.[115] Narrow white borders emphasised the outlines of the keel arches and broader bands of white also framed the edges of the wall and staircases. This difference in colour can be seen as an attempt to echo the white lines and surfaces of the marble scales in the building and thus create a certain uniformity. In this respect, the model of the Great Samrat Yantra is similar in style to the Small Samrat Yantra, as the latter is the only building to have all its parts outlined in white even today.

Today, the Great Samrat Yantra is painted a uniform yellow; there are no white outlines and intrados. One of Kaye's photographs reveals that the Rashi Valaya Yantras were outlined in white in his day.[116] Hendley's models are also outlined in white and have bright red stonework. We can therefore assume that many of the instruments have had coloured paint outlined in white since at least the 19th century.

From the similar colouring of the Small Samrat Yantra, it might be concluded that this paint and the model of the Great Samrat Yantra date from Maharaja Ram Singh's day, but it may also be a model from Jai Singh's lifetime, as the white outlines are borrowed from Mogul architecture and were frequently used in Jai Singh's day, for example in his palace and on many of the façades of houses in Jaipur.

The model is built to the unusual scale of 1:24. This scale only makes any sense in the Indian measuring system, indicating a local model builder, and not Kaye, Garrett or any other European restorer.

Models of the Small Samrat Yantra (figs. 115–119)

There is a brass model which corresponds closely to the Small Samrat Yantra. The only visible difference is that in the model there are four keel arches set into the meridian wall, while in the building there are only three (figs. 115, 117, 118).

Of the four arches in the model, let us examine the three of the four arches which form a symmetrical group, a large one in the centre and two

114 As the author felt that these models were all extremely valuable historical records, he suggested to the relevant department of the government of Rajasthan that they should be moved to the palace museum. They are currently being stored inside the Narivalaya Uttar Gola.

115 The photo in figure 114 was taken when the original version had already been repainted grey.

116 Plate XX, fig. 54 in G. R. Kaye, *The Astronomical Observatories of Jai Singh*, Calcutta, 1918.

Fig. 115 Brass model of the Small Samrat Yantra, Jaipur, to a scale of 1:48. It shows the original design of the Small Samrat Yantra, from which the present-day building deviates.

Fig. 116   Wooden model of the Small Samrat Yantra, Jaipur, to a scale of 1:40. This preliminary design for the Small Samrat Yantra was never built.

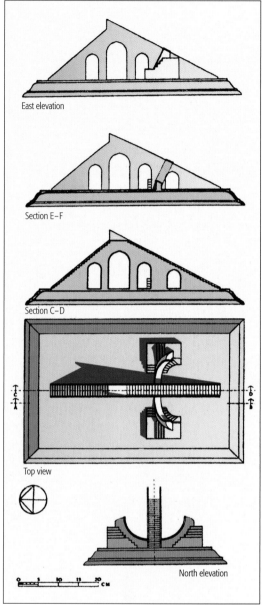

East elevation

Section E–F

Section C–D

Top view

North elevation

Fig. 117   Brass model of the Small Samrat Yantra, Jaipur.

smaller ones at the side. The small arches also appear in the building itself, but the large one in the centre is missing. It now seems reasonable to conclude that the model shows the planned design and that before or during the construction it was decided to wall up the central opening, presumably because it was thought the building would be unstable if the marble scales were only supported by a lightweight archway.

The model undoubtedly shows a more elegant, lighter-looking solution. In harmony with the external outline, the row of arches begins and ends with a small keel arch whilst the large central arch forms the visual centre of the construction. This rhythm is not repeated in the building, and we might wonder why, after the decision was taken to drop the central arch, the smaller arches were not moved towards the

Fig. 118   Model of the Small Samrat Yantra, Jaipur, to a scale of 1:48.

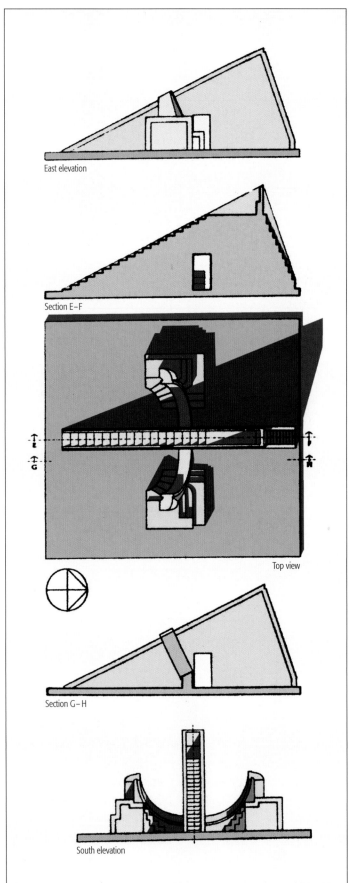

East elevation

Section E–F

Top view

Section G–H

South elevation

centre – in particular the north one which is set too close to the outside edge – in order to have a single, visually pleasing wall surface enclosing the arches. One explanation is that the decision to leave out the central arch was only taken during the construction period. But certainly it must have been well before the wall was covered with red sandstone. The dimensions of the stone slabs, their position and their uniform finish preclude the building having been altered after completion.[117]

The model certainly predates the building. Severin Noti puts the date of the building as 1876,[118] during the reign of the Maharaja Ram Singh. The scale of the model, 1:50, is arrived at by comparing the radii of the quadrants both in the building and in the model (2.78 metres and 0.056 metres). Since this scale would presuppose the only recently introduced metric system, the model was probably planned to a scale of 1:48, more in accordance with the Indian system of measurement.

There is one other model of the Small Samrat Yantra in Jaipur, to a scale of 1:40 and made of wood (figs. 116 and 119). This model differs in many of its details from the building itself and must therefore have been meant either as an unused preliminary model for the Small Samrat Yantra or else as a design for a different building which was never constructed. It is unlikely that they intended to build a third Samrat Yantra in Jaipur, since the building of the Small Samrat Yantra was basically already superfluous and they had more suitable instruments for measuring the paths of the stars in India at the end of the 19th century. This suggests therefore that the wooden model is even older than the brass one.

117 See also p. 139 on the subject of bonding the stones.
118 Accepted by Garrett.

Fig. 119 Wooden model of the Small Samrat Yantra, Jaipur.

Fig. 120   This is one of a number of models of the Narivalaya Uttar Gola, Jaipur, that were discovered amongst the rubble that fills some of the rooms of the observatory.

Models of the Narivalaya Uttar Gola (figs. 120–122)

The pandit in the observatory at Jaipur has in his charge a wooden model of the Narivalaya Uttar Gola. A plaster model of this same structure was also found under the rubble in a ground-floor room of the Dakshino Bhitti Yantra. The latter model differs from the building in the following

details: the doors are missing on the east and west side; on the south side, instead of two walls which appear in both the building and the wooden model, there is a small polos. The drum-shaped sundial on the roof is also not shown in the plaster model.

Jagannath writes: 'This instrument is not very useful, as only the stars appearing to the north of the equator can be observed',[119] implying that

119   Jagganath, *Samrat Siddhanta*.

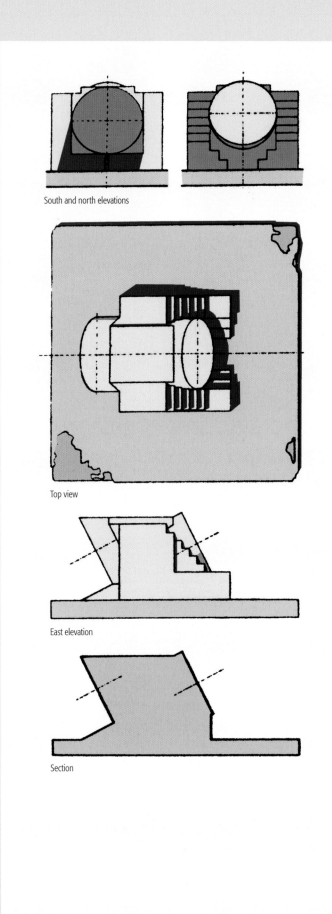

South and north elevations

Top view

East elevation

Section

Fig. 121   Plaster and sandstone
model of the Narivalaya Uttar Gola, Jaipur.

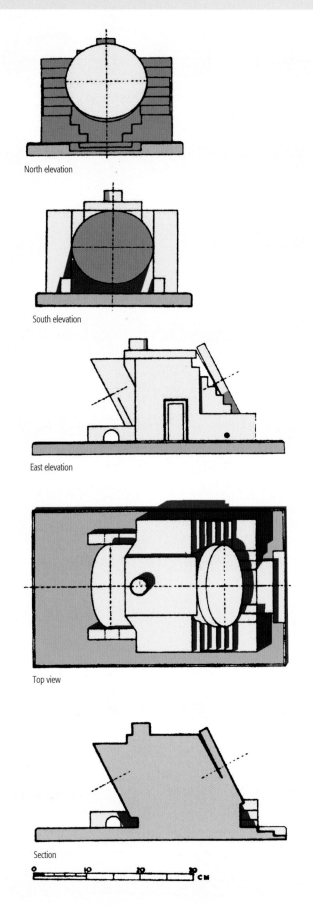

North elevation

South elevation

East elevation

Top view

Section

Fig. 122   Wooden model of the Narivalaya Uttar Gola, Jaipur.

in Jai Singh's day only the north-facing sundial on the Narivalaya Uttar Gola existed. Garrett[120] presumes that the southern extension dated from the reign of the Maharaja Pratab Singh (1778–1803).[121] Gokul Chandra Bhawan[122] also endorses this view, since Pratab Singh is mentioned in the seventh line of an inscription in the building, although together with the year of restoration AD 1718. The stonemason who engraved the inscription must have made a mistake with the date, since the town and palace of Jaipur were not even under construction in 1718.

The white plaster model was not built after the extension of the Narivalaya Uttar Gola, since it differs from the extended building in the details mentioned above. Neither can it stem from Jai Singh's day, since the alterations are already shown. The model shows how the real thing might have been built and should therefore be given a date in the reign of Pratab Singh as a draft for the alterations. The choice of a scale of 1:36 again points to a local model builder.[123]

The wooden model of the Narivalaya Uttar Gola is less carefully made than the other models. Arabic numbers on the circular scales suggest that it is from a later date, and was possibly built by a European, except that the scale of 1:24 again points to a local model maker.

Model of the Rashi Valaya Yantras (figs. 123–125)

The model of the twelve Rashi Valaya Yantras is made of wood and sheet brass. The model only differs from the buildings in terms of the site plan, the relative distances between the yantras being different.

In the model, as in the buildings, the rounded corners of the 'Scorpio' and 'Pisces' instruments catch the eye; these were necessary because these two yantras are too close to 'Capricorn'. Why did they build three yantras so close together that there would have been no way through if they had been given the normal unrounded shape? This is particularly puzzling given the wide gaps between the remaining Rashi Valaya Yantras.

The Rashi Valaya Yantras could have been built in one row of twelve, in two rows of six, in three rows of four instruments, etc. They could also have been built in a wide circle so that they would stand next to one another like the animals in the sign of the zodiac. A third possibility can be inferred from the function of the Rashi Valaya Yantras: as their role was to provide data for horoscopes, why not erect the instruments according to the positions of the signs of the zodiac or of the houses in the square horoscope? The plan of the site would appear to confirm this (fig. 86). The diagram in fig. 124 shows, in spite of all the irregularities in the sequence, the clockwise movement starting from the east. The diagram in fig. 125 shows the position of the instruments in relation to each other, but without the 'Aquarius' and 'Gemini' instruments being out of line (the reasons for this irregular layout have been given earlier).[124] The result is a symmetrical picture which is similar to a horoscope chart. The latter also has an open space in the middle, which is often assigned to the highest principle in the mandala, and the cardinal points are occupied by those signs which divide the year into quarters by equinoxes and solstices. In addition, the Aries, Cancer, Libra and Capricorn signs stand out because their quadrant radii are greater (1.683 metres) than those of the normal signs (1.243 metres).

The site plan does admittedly differ from the horoscope chart in two ways: first of all by the unexplained compression and rounding off of instruments nos. 8 and 12 and, secondly, by the similarly unexplained set-back position of the odd-numbered signs 3, 5, 9 and 11.

A comparison of the quadrant radii of all the Rashi Valaya Yantras offers an explanation for

120 A. Garrett and Ch. Guleri, *The Jaipur Observatory and its Builder*, Allahabad, 1902.
121 According to James Tod, *Annals and Antiquities of Rajasthan*, vol. 2, London, 1832.
122 In Gokul Chandra Bhawan, *Samrat Yantra*, Jaipur, n.d., p. 45.
123 The author has reconstructed all units of measurement. This also allows for a reconstruction of the scales of all models.
124 See p. 65.

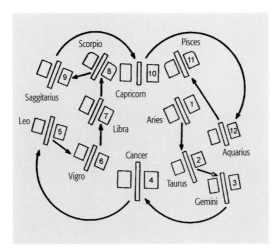

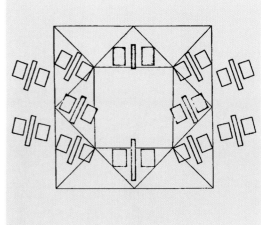

Fig. 124   Diagram showing the layout of the Rashi Valaya Yantras in Jaipur.

Fig. 125   Diagram of the horoscope showing the position of the twelve Rashi Valaya Yantras.

125   See note 123.
126   Tieffenthaler mentions all 12 Rashi Valaya Yantras in his description of the observatory, see p. 65
127   The complicated staircases on the quadrants of the Great Samrat Yantra in Jaipur are examples of this.

this irregularity. Only the four signs situated at the four cardinal points have quadrant radii which correspond to the contemporary system of measurement (r = 1.683 m = 2 cubits at 0.843 m).[125] That suggests that the Aries, Cancer, Libra and Capricorn signs were built first and that they only added the remaining signs later (but before Tieffenthaler's visit to Jaipur),[126] without any precise knowledge of the original system of measuring or the intended overall shape.

Thus, a non-functional pattern relating to the representation of the zodiac can be recognised in the site plan, but the execution, which took place in two construction phases, differs from this pattern for reasons unknown.

Model of a Rama Yantra
(figs. 126, 128)

This wooden model of one of the Rama Yantras resembles in all but a few details the Eastern Great Rama Yantra in Jaipur. The foundations for the stairs leading to the round top of the building are not broken up by a keel arch in the model.

Moreover, the whole staircase appears to have been added on after the model was made. We know this because the staircase hides a series of horizontal slots in the masonry (fig. 128). These slots in the pillars were intended to permit the insertion of observation platforms at different heights – the only way to get the eye close enough to any point on the edges of the graduated areas. The staircase was the same width as a stone pillar, which meant they could not insert more observation platforms on either side of the stairs. As a result, in the building there are no slots in the masonry of the pillar adjoining the stairs.

One might conclude from these observations that the staircase in the model was built before that of the building. Since access to the horizontal level at the top was necessary in order to stretch the wires holding the gnomon which point to the four main compass points, one might further assume that the staircase was already built in Jai Singh's day. To reach the top level, even from a platform fitted into the top slots, some gymnastics would have been necessary. But the maharaja obviously set particularly great store by having easy access to all the instruments.[127]

If the horizontal graduated areas in the model had been shown with foundations, it would

Fig. 123   Wooden model of the twelve Rashi Valaya Yantras, Jaipur.

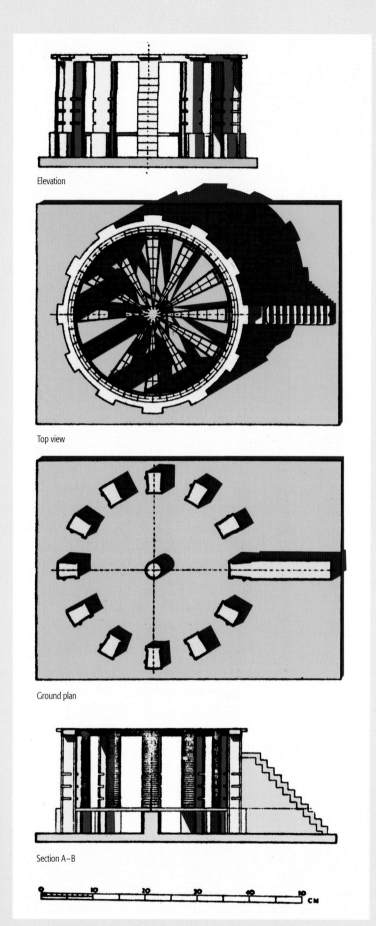

Elevation

Top view

Ground plan

Section A–B

Fig. 126   Wooden model of the Rama Yantra, Jaipur.

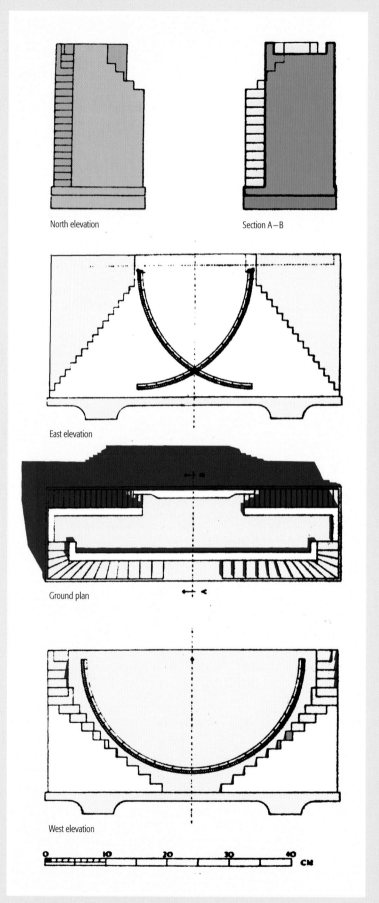

North elevation

Section A–B

East elevation

Ground plan

West elevation

Fig. 127   White marble model of the Dakshino Bhitti Yantra, Jaipur.

Fig. 128   A wooden model of the Rama Yantra.

that the original Rama Yantra presumably had no staircase. From a comparison of the lengths of the vertical graduated areas (0.1444 and 3.442 metres), the scale works out at 1:24.

To the south-east of the Great Rama Yantra in Jaipur, there are two Small Rama Yantras which can also be regarded as pilot schemes for the final version. They naturally have no staircase to the top level and no slots in the masonry for platforms.

A comparison of measurements produces the following scales: the wooden model and the Small Rama Yantras, 1:6; the Small Rama Yantras and the Great Rama Yantras, 1:4.

Model of the Dakshino Bhitti Yantra (figs. 127, 129)

Possibly the most beautiful of the models known to have survived is that of the Dakshino Bhitti Yantra. It is hewn like a monolith out of a block of white marble. Doors, windows and staircase balustrades are not represented in the model. Is it a representation of the shape of the building which was subsequently simplified or is it a preliminary draft?

The sandstone balustrades which make the building's staircase safe today are composed of slabs placed side by side. The balustrade was only added after the completion of the staircase, i.e. the lower edge of the slabs was made to fit the outline of the steps. To the south side of the Dakshino Bhitti Yantra, we see a balustrade slab revealing some of these rectangular tooth-like cuts which, however, do not match the steps. From that we can conclude that this slab had already been part of the balustrade at an earlier date but was in a different position. (The slab cannot have belonged to a different instrument, because only the Dakshino Bhitti Yantra has a balustrade of this shape.) The first date which

therefore have been reasonable to date the model to Jai Singh's day because this construction would only have been possible if the circular sectors had been made of stone. But Garrett expressly states that the Rama Yantras in Jaipur were originally built in brick and plaster stucco and were only given stone scales in 1891.[128] Consequently, the wooden model is without doubt a draft for the alterations carried out in 1891, with the exception of the keel arch opening in the staircase. That means that a staircase was only decided on during this planning stage and

128   A. Garrett and Ch. Guleri, *The Jaipur Observatory and its Builder*, Allahabad, 1902.

Fig. 129   Marble model of the Dakshino Bhitti Yantra in Jaipur. View of the eastern meridian wall, scale: 1:32.

springs to mind for the re-use of this old piece of balustrade is 1876, when they moved the building (see page 65). This means that the Dakshino Bhitti also had a sandstone balustrade in its original position.

If the marble model had been made at the time the Dakshino Bhitti Yantra was moved, as a copy of the old building and a draft for the new one, then they would certainly also have portrayed the original balustrades. One is therefore in-

clined to regard the model as a preliminary draft from Jai Singh's day with no windows or doors. It is a perfect example of a local monolithic model which was certainly not produced in the workshops of the English restorers.

The scale cannot be determined with any certainty. If the radii of the circular scales or the width of the model and the building are compared, then we get the scale of 1:33, if their height and length are compared, then we get the

Models of the Jai Prakash Yantras
(figs. 130–132)

There are several models of the Jai Prakash Yantras:

(1) A sandstone model, preserved in fragments, corresponds to the northern Great Jai Prakash Yantra. A comparison of the radii of the spheres (r = 0.1135 metres and r = 2.72 metres) gives a scale of 1:24.

(2) The second, a drum-shaped model (fig. 132), is in better condition. The hour circles starting from the projection of the celestial north pole are at intervals of 6°, whereas they are at 15° intervals (1 hour) in the building and the sandstone fragment. Given that there are no gaps and that comparison of the sphere's radii does not produce any sensible ratio, it appears not to be a draft model for the Great Prakash Yantra. Given the distance between the hour lines, the model corresponds to the Small Jai Prakash Yantra, which is set into a low platform to the west of the Great Jai Prakash Yantra along with the Kapali Yantra. A comparison of the radii of the sphere produces the scale of 1:12, proving conclusively that the drum-shaped model is indeed part of the Small Jai Prakash Yantra.

The building admittedly does not match the model in every detail. In the former, the hemisphere is divided into 15 vertical circles of 6°, and in the model into 18 vertical circles of 5°. The model cannot be seen as a later copy; it possibly portrays the original condition of the Small Jai Prakash Yantra when the scales made by Jai Singh in white plaster stucco had still not been replaced by marble ones.

(3) A further dish-shaped sandstone model of a Jai Prakash Yantra (fig. 130) shows, through black line-drawing, the geometrical division of the northern Great Jai Prakash Yantra right down to such details as the pattern of the gaps in the stone around the projected celestial north pole. In many respects it is similar to the sandstone fragment. Both models are made from the same

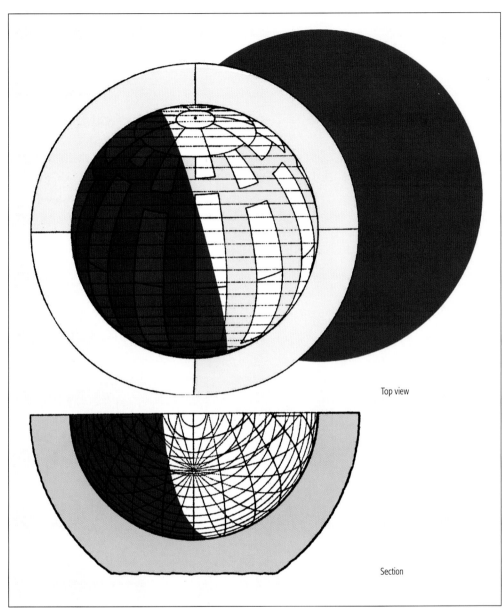

Top view

Section

Fig. 130   Dish-shaped sandstone model of the Jai Prakash Yantra, Jaipur.

scale of 1:32. The scale 1:33 is inconceivable in the English and the Indian systems of measuring, since it presupposes a metric system. The model was probably built to the scale of 1:32, which is somewhat unusual for India, and an alteration in the proportions only resulted when the Dakshino Bhitti Yantra was moved.

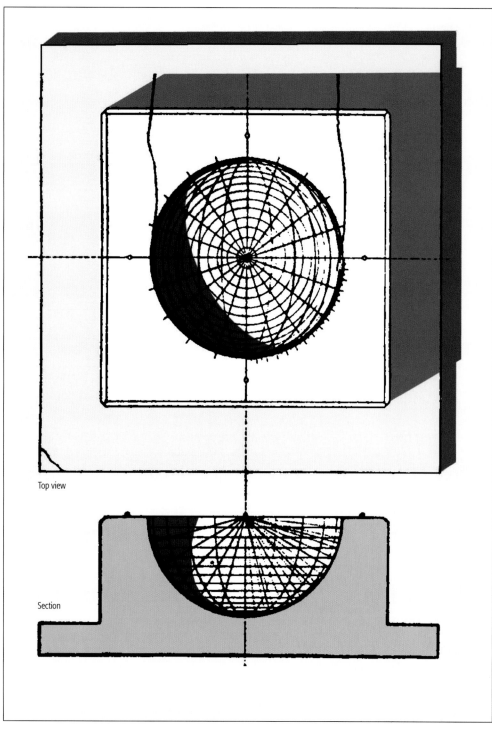

Top view

Section

Fig. 131   Plaster model of the Kapali Yantra, Jaipur.

sandstone covered with a thin layer of plaster, but they do not form a whole in the same way as the two Great Jai Prakash Yantras (see page 53). In both models, the same parts of the sphere are provided with walk-in gaps.

The dimensions of the individual pieces of marble out of which the hemisphere was made are clearly defined on the dish-shaped sandstone model. It cannot date from Jai Singh's day, since he had the parts of the sphere made of white stucco. We have no documentary evidence as to when the plaster scales were replaced by marble ones, so it is impossible to put a date on the model.

(4) Another model, which has an octagonal ground plan, does not reveal any traces of cracks or lacquer on the surface of the sphere. Only the four places for attaching cross wires suggest that it was a Jai Prakash Yantra. A comparison of the radii of the spheres (0.151 metres and 2.72 metres) suggests that it relates to the Great Jai Prakash Yantra on a scale of 1:18.

(5) A fifth model (fig. 131) obviously was designed to test the usefulness of the Small Jai Prakash Yantra presented in fig. 50.

Model of the Unnatansha Yantra

A rosewood model of the Unnatansha Yantra is similar to the building in its structure but not in its proportions and material. The treatment of the wood with inlaid brass suggests an English client or manufacturer. The figures on the hanging brass ring are engraved in Arabic numerals. The whole gives the impression of being a souvenir rather than a draft model. A comparison of the principal dimensions gives a ratio of 1:18.

Model of the Digamsa Yantra (fig. 133)

The model of the Digamsa Yantra is made of sandstone and plaster and only differs from the building in two details: the gateways in the outer circular wall end in round arches in the model, but have a horizontal lintel in the building (fig. 43); eight seats attached to the circular wall in the middle are missing in the building. The model may show the building in an earlier state or it could be a preliminary draft that dates from Jai Singh's day.

Fig. 132   Drum-shaped sandstone and plaster model of the Great Jai Prakash Yantra, Jaipur.

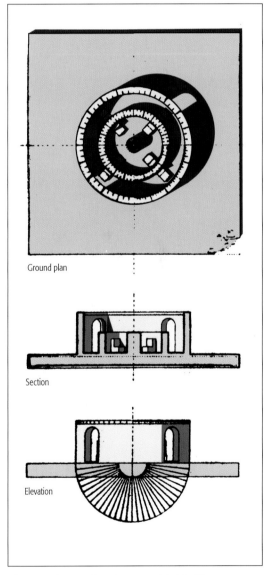

Ground plan

Section

Elevation

Fig. 133   Plaster and sandstone model of the Digamsa Yantra, Jaipur.

5 | Construction Methods

Although most of the instruments at the observatories in Delhi, Jaipur, Benares and Ujjain have been continuously restored and partially rebuilt, we can still draw conclusions about the building methods and materials used in Jai Singh's day. Even today, the walls consist of the original quarrystone and mortar. This same limestone mortar was also used for smoothing down the rough masonry. Jai Singh himself gives 'stone and limestone' as the materials used in his observatory in Delhi.[129]

Only one comment on the building techniques has survived from the architect Jagannath. He describes the building of the Small Jai Prakash Yantra as follows:

> Draw a circle of any radius with a compass on a level piece of ground and draw in the north-south and the east-west diameters. Then dig a hole roughly in the shape of a hemisphere with the diameter of the circle. Make a semicircle out of wood or iron and rotate it in the hollow. If the semicircle touches all points of the hollow as it rotates then the instrument has been correctly made.[130]

More contemporary details, particularly about the materials, are found in the description of the Jaipur observatory by Tieffenthaler.[131] According to his observations, there were Rashi Valaya Yantras 'of pure limestone... astrolabes also made of limestone... and a horizontal sundial carved into a very large stone... a very tall, thick axis of the celestial sphere made of bricks and limestone'. He describes the quadrants of the Samrat Yantra as 'a very skilful piece of work in the whitest limestone or plaster', and the Shastansha Yantra as 'similarly made of plaster'.

Two of his statements are erroneous. The thick axis of the celestial sphere, by which he means the Great Samrat Yantra, is not built of brick but of quarrystone. Tieffenthaler only saw the Samrat Yantra when it had been plastered over and probably thought of brick when he saw the plastered masonry. The other mistake, concerning the horizontal sundial, has already been noted.[132]

'Pure limestone' and 'whitest limestone' do not mean limestone or marble, but limestone plaster. The quadrants of the Shastansha Yantra are also described by Garrett as being made of plaster and those of the Great Samrat Yantra as being of fine Chunam plaster.[133]

There are no references to white marble and red sandstone, the two preferred materials in Mogul architecture, to be found in any written sources from Jai Singh's day. Obviously these two materials were only used after the construction of the Small Samrat Yantra under Maharaja Ram Singh.

Only in the Benares observatory did Jai Singh use a durable material for his instruments. Sir Robert Barker, writing from Benares in 1777, made the following observations:

> The execution in the construction of these instruments exhibited a mathematical exactness in the fixing, bearing, and fitting of the several parts, in the necessary and sufficient supports to the very large stones that composed them, and in the joining and fastening each into the other by means of lead and iron.[134]

An examination by the author of the various samples of stone and plaster from the Jaipur observatory revealed:

129 See quotation p. 67.
130 *Samrat Siddhanta* by Jagganath.
131 Joseph Tieffenthaler, *Beschreibung von Hindustan*, translated into German by J. Bernoulli, Berlin, 1785.
132 See p. 65.
133 A. Garrett and Ch. Guleri, *The Jaipur Observatory and its Builder*, Allahabad, 1902.
134 R. Barker, 'An Account of the Bramin's Observatory at Benares', in *Philosophical Transactions of the Royal Society of London*, vol. 67, part II, London, 1777, p. 599f.

Fig. 134   A network of water channels was created on the base of the Samrat Yantra in Jaipur. The surface of the water served as a reference plane to adjust the measuring scales (spirit levels were unknown at the time). Similar channels were planned for the quadrants of the Rama Yantras, which were never built.

stone, and the mortar has only a small amount of lime material as a binder.[139]

5. The internal rooms of the Dakshino Bhitti Yantra were originally only stuccoed with a thin layer of fine white plaster.[140] The fine red plaster visible today was applied to the sooty surface in two layers at a later date.

Construction Method for the Great Rama Yantras

The Great Rama Yantras of Jaipur both stand on a circular platform (figs. 95, 96). As we have seen (see page 99), the order in which the quartzite blocks on the platform were laid can be seen from the stone plan. First of all, they laid the stones for the east-west axis, then those for the north-south axis and then those of the circle marking the boundary of the platform. Before they began to build up the quadrants, they presumably filled them with water so as to check the horizontal. Construction was carried out in a systematic fashion, with a strip placed east to west in each quadrant, then another strip placed from north to south. They proceeded alternately in this way until the surfaces were filled in.

In the Western Great Rama Yantra, in which the scales are 12° wide and the gaps between the pillars 18° wide, they carved into the platform the boundary lines of the planned circular sectors situated above them. Four further lines, as indicated in the stone plan, established the width of the plinths of the pillars at 10° and that of the stone supports inside the building at 11°. In the middle, they erected a column made out of two stones pinned together. The stone supports of the circular scale were erected in two concentric rings and in a third outside ring they built the plinths of the pillars to the same height.

To make the plinths, they used the typical Indian method of joining stones without mortar.

1. The red cladding of the Small Samrat Yantra consists of quartzite.[135]
2. The white outlines of all the parts of the Small Samrat Yantra are made of quartzite,[136] but the scales are of marble (fig. 62).[137]
3. The horizontal stone sectors of the Great Rama Yantras consist of quartzite (fig. 41).[138]
4. The aggregate of the bright red mortar, which appears in the same compound in the stonework of the Great Samrat Yantra, the Small Samrat Yantra, the Dakshino Bhitti Yantra and the Kranti Writta, is not crushed brick but very rough red sand-

135   With a lot of iron-hydroxide pigment, about 10% impurities, no mica, occasional feldspars, no indication of direction, size of grains 50μ–150μ.
136   Without impurities, with sharp edges to the grain, size of grains 100μ–150μ, no indication of direction, no metamorphic structures.
137   Sugar-grain marble without impurities.
138   Few pigments, hence yellowish colour, size of grains 50μ–150μ, no indication of direction, silicate binder.
139   An analysis of all materials was carried out by the author in 1969.
140   That is, after its removal to the present position.

A layer of tall blocks is followed by a layer of thin flat stone slabs, which act as a course of headers. The Pallavas had used the same technique in the 7th century AD in southern India for building the Kailasanatha and Virupaksha temples in Kanchipuram, although this was for theological as well as structural reasons.[141]

In the next stage, they placed the stone sectors of the circular scales on to the plinths and stone supports. To get the circular scale horizontal, they simply referred to the platform which had already been adjusted. This is demonstrated by the fact that the distance between the level of the scales and the platform reveals only small variations. The absolute height of the scales, however, varies to a much greater degree.

Only at this point did they start to build up the wall pillars to their final height, join them by a circular anchor and install the vertical scales on the inside.

A thin stone slab juts out from the circular anchor above each of the wall pillars in such a way as to form the shape of a cogwheel. In heavy rain, these slabs act as overhangs so the water drips away from the stonework. A slight slope in the upper surface of the circular anchor ensures that the water does not run down the inside of the wall pillar and over the scales. Eaves of this type, known as 'chaya' in India, are an integral part of Hindu buildings. They are usually placed in a circle right round the house close to the upper edge of the wall of flat-roofed buildings; occasionally they are also found simply as short planks above the doors and windows.

In the days of the Islamic sultans of Delhi, the architects often did without this traditional feature which gave protection from sun and rain. The first Moguls did not use them either. But under Akbar, who promoted an Islamic style of building influenced by Hinduism, the planks were revived. In Fatehpur Sikri, the royal capital hurriedly built between 1569 and 1585 for Akbar, they were to be found on every build-ing.[142] In their palaces, the late Moguls replaced the *chayas* supported by consoles with ones supported by a continuous hollow moulding.[143] This newer form of canopy was copied in the Jaipur observatory on the so-called 'Astro-nomer's House'.

The *chayas* of the Great Rama Yantras do not have the customary slope of around 20°. There may be different reasons for this deviation from tradition. Either the original *chayas* were more steeply sloping and were not made with a gentler slope until the completed renovation of the Rama Yantras in 1891,[144] or the architects simply disliked the idea of providing their geometrically constructed Rama Yantras with twelve small slanting roofs.

Bonding the Stone

From around the 10th century AD in northern India, iron braces were often used for fixing rectangular blocks of stone together without mortar. The braces were usually only used for horizontal joins, as layers were not usually joined vertically.

In Jai Singh's observatories, they used the same technique when they built certain parts not with quarrystone and mortar but with stone blocks joined without mortar (this type of bracing was described by J. L. Williams).[145] Occasionally, as for example on the protruding underside of a marble scale in the southern Great Jai Prakash Yantra in Jaipur (fig. 135), one can also see marble braces shaped like a double T. They presumably chose stone braces instead of the simpler iron ones because they were more pleasing to the eye and less inconspicuous.

For some instruments in Jaipur and Benares, they devised a particularly durable and expen-sive way of joining stones without mortar: they cut the stones with irregular denticulations. This was done with such precision that in the zig-zag

141 See the author's *Living Architecture: Indian*, New York and London, 1969, p. 182.
142 See the author's *Living Architecture: Islamic Indian*, New York and London,1970, p. 21.
143 For example, at the Diwan-i-Khas in the Red Fort of Delhi.
144 The same design on the Small Samrat Yantra contradicts this hypothesis.
145 J. L. Williams, 'Further Particulars Respect-ing the Observatory at Benares', *Philo-sophical Transactions of the Royal Society of London*, MDCCXCIII, part I, London, 1793, p. 46.

join there was not even a millimetre to spare. This procedure was obviously adapted from carpentry. Another technique, tongue and groove, was also borrowed from carpentry. It was particularly suitable for joining together the slabs used for

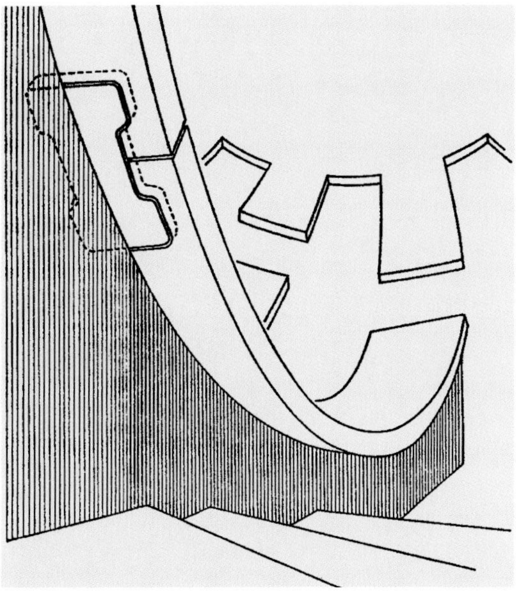

Fig. 135 To bond individual pieces of marble, double T-shaped stone braces were occasionally used, as here in one of the Great Jai Prakash Yantras.

lining walls. All the slabs lining the Small Samrat Yantra have been put together using a joint on the edge of the slabs.

An observer unfamiliar with the history of Indian architecture might assume from the use of such techniques that the building of the yantras had been carried out not by bricklayers and masons but by carpenters. After all, it would not have been the first time that craftsmen expert in other materials had worked in stone. In Sanchi, the well-preserved Buddhist shrine dating from the 3rd century BC, an inscription on one of the *toranas* of the Great Stupa says that the ivory carvers from Visisha had made and donated the stone gateway.

A look at Hindu building methods, however, shows that the stonemasons of India also wanted to maintain two very old traditional construction methods: in the south of the subcontinent, megalithic building techniques, which still influence construction methods today; in the north, bamboo and wood construction methods (for example, the wooden frames copied in monolithic stone in the prayer halls in Ajanta and Ellora). Some buildings of the observatories, notably the Small Samrat Yantra in Jaipur, offer further evidence of the tradition of stonemasons working in stone but still thinking in terms of carpentry techniques.

The Small Samrat Yantra contains another interesting detail: in the sandstone lining, the alternation of thin horizontal layers with thick layers is more clear than in the stone plinths of the Great Samrat Yantra. These layers are formed not by large blocks, but by lining slabs. The thin layers are courses of headers and go deep into the quarrystone masonry. The slabs of the lining are also attached to them by the tongue and groove method. Wall linings of this type are typical of the architecture of the Great Moguls. The earliest example is the Humayun monument in Delhi, a tomb in the Persian style from the days of Akbar, translated into Indian building techniques and materials. Later examples are the walls of the Red Fort in Delhi and the Fort of Agra.

Staircases

In the days of the Great Moguls, little importance was attached to creating an easy gradient for stairs. Formal and not practical considerations were of paramount importance. The stairs in the Pearl Mosque in Agra, for example, were built in the narrowest of spaces between different landings and they turned out to be extraordinarily steep. In Delhi, too, in the Humayun tomb, it

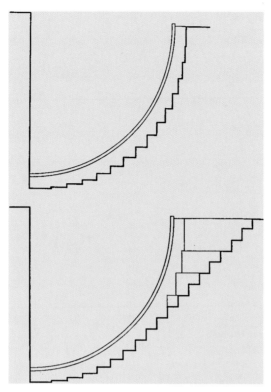

Fig. 136 When the course of the staircase follows the quadrants of the Samrat Yantras at a constant distance from the marble scale, the upper steps are inaccessible.

required great effort to climb one of the four main staircases to the actual tomb situated in the axes of the platform. In view of the fact that the locals tend to be smaller than Europeans, the gradient chosen for the stairs appears particularly steep.

The stairs in Jai Singh's observatories are also steeper than our present-day stairs. In some cases, however, their gradient stemmed inevitably from the shape and function of the instruments. The stairs along the marble quadrants of the Great Samrat Yantra of Jaipur, for example, begin with wide treads and very low risers. Following the course of the quadrant they become steeper and steeper until, at the upper end of the quadrant, the ratio is finally reversed so that the last steps are impossible to use. They appear like narrow platforms piled on top of each other, only accessible via 'secondary stairs' which are built along the excessively high risers of the

'primary staircase'. The 'secondary stairs' are so skilfully joined to the 'primary' ones that one is hardly aware of the transition and the upper steps of the 'primary staircase' actually look like elements which have been added on.

In the Samrat Yantras in Jaipur, Delhi, Benares and Ujjain, the gradient of those stairs which lead via the upper edge to the top of the building is determined in each case by the local geographical latitude. In Jaipur, the steps on the Small Samrat Yantra had a riser/tread average of 15.9/30.7 centimetres, in Delhi 28.2/34.0 centimetres, in Benares 18.5/42.0 centimetres and in Ujjain 17.5/42.5 centimetres.

Those staircases whose dimensions were not determined by structural considerations could be described as having 'normal' gradients. This applies, for example, to the stairs which lead from the west on to the west tower of the Great Samrat Yantra of Delhi and those which lead from the east on to the east tower. Both sets of stairs have an average gradient of 32.0/31.3 centimetres; that is, the risers are higher than the treads are wide. Stairs in the Small Samrat Yantra of Jaipur, whose measurements are also not determined by any other elements of the building, have a similar gradient ratio, 31.0/30.3 centimetres.

It can be seen from this small selection of typical staircases that Jai Singh's architects, when designing a staircase, did not start out with a comfortable gradient in mind but took, as their idea of a staircase, a sequence of horizontal and vertical lines of equal length which rose at 45°. It is not only in children's drawings that we encounter this particular style of staircase – noteworthy only in so far as it is practically never used in the West. Adults also usually draw 'Indian staircases' like this when they are asked to draw a diagram of the side view of a staircase.

Apart from their steepness, the various staircases in the observatories also differ in shape. The variations in shape are partly determined by the building material, but they also indicate that different architects worked on the observatory at different times.

In Jai Singh's day, when the majority of the instruments were made in quarrystone and were lined afterwards with a layer of plaster 15 centimetres thick, they treated the treads and risers in the same way as all the other wall surfaces. Staircases made in this way are to be seen on

both sides of the Great Samrat Yantras in Delhi and Jaipur, on the Narivalaya Uttar Gola and on the Kranti Writta in Jaipur. They are painted in the same colour as the whole building, rather like the staircases in housing complexes in Mediterranean countries. The treads and risers are not independent constructional elements which contrast with the whole building, but simply spatially differentiated parts of the same.

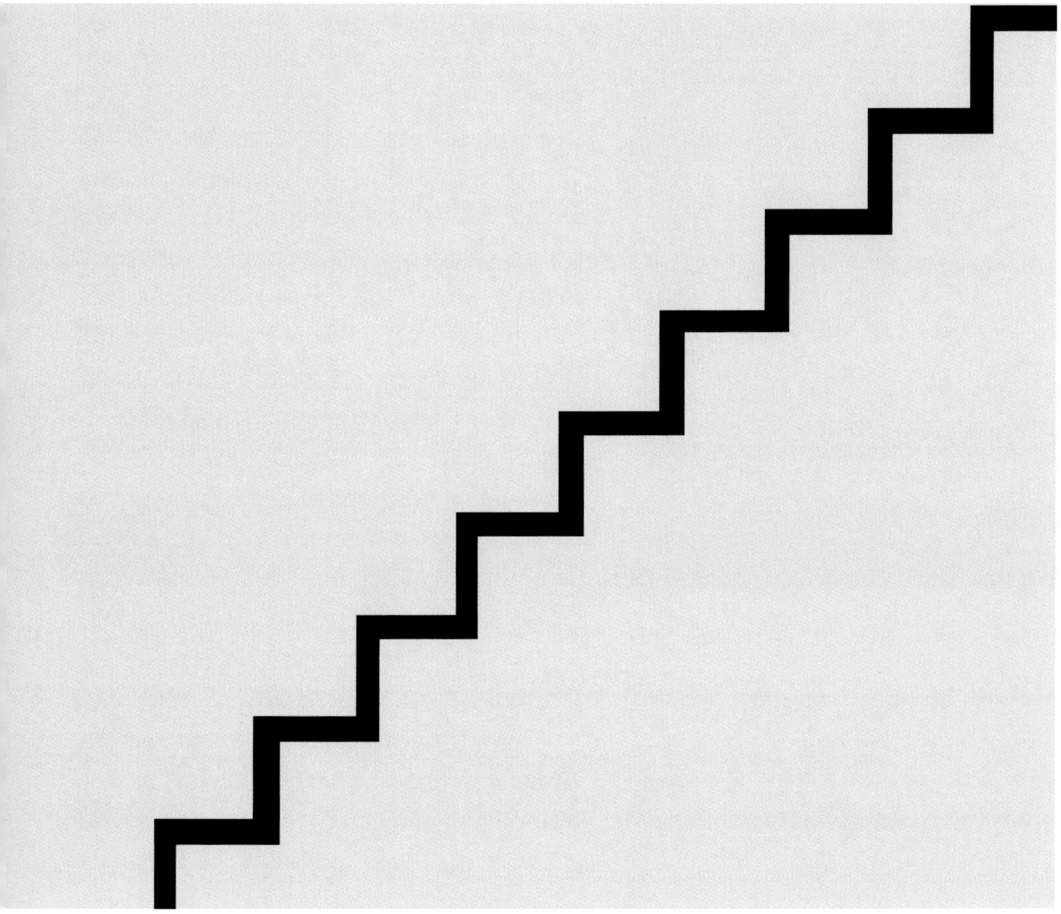

They built staircases of quite a different type for one of the Rashi Valaya Yantras. For the instrument assigned to Cancer, instead of the normal plastered quarrystone, unplastered ashlar was chosen (fig. 138). The staircases are not built in a uniform way. Steps made of blocks follow sections of stairs clearly broken up into treads and risers; and while the staircase leading from the south on to the meridian wall is connected to the structural framework of the layers of blocks and headers, the staircase coming from the north stands out clearly from the masonry bond, accentuated by treads and risers with decorated hollow mouldings. Logically, this accentuation of the outline is abandoned at the point where the steps lead into the meridian wall. From there on, broad steps made of blocks run right through the meridian wall. The profiles of both staircases stand out against the network of joins in the wall. From this it can be seen that in the construction of the Rashi Valaya Yantra attributed to Cancer the meridian wall was made first along with the stairs up to the height of the top tread and in the second stage they laid the marble scales and the foundations of their walls.

The staircases which run alongside the marble quadrants on to the platforms of the Cancer instrument are also broken up into treads and risers. In this respect they are like the staircase of the Small Samrat Yantra of Jaipur. Admittedly there the uniform white outline round all the parts of the building covered in red inevitably means that the staircases which are framed in the

Fig. 137   The staircases built in the observatories were often of the simplest type, with treads and risers of equal length, even though they are difficult to climb.

Fig. 138   The steps leading to the Cancer Rashi Valaya Yantra stand out amid the network of joints in the masonry.

horizontal and vertical wall surfaces. It cannot be coincidental that the Small Samrat Yantra, if it could be seen from above, would consist entirely of white surfaces.[146] On the other hand, viewed from the ground it consists entirely of red surfaces framed in white. This different treatment of the horizontal and vertical planes is extended right down to each individual step. From the side view, the step appears as a white outline, but viewed from the front the risers once again look like small red panels.

The solid, amorphous character of the older stone staircases is in direct contrast to this subtly differentiated creative mode, whose elements are taken directly from the architecture of the Great Moguls. Changes in theories concerning architectural symbolism – one and a half centuries separate the oldest and the newest buildings – meant that two instruments of the same kind, such as the two Samrat Yantras of Jaipur or the Rama Yantras of Jaipur and Delhi, appear to have little in common with each other.

Wages and Building Costs

same way stand out (see page 64): if the observer concentrates his gaze on the outline of the red sandstone surfaces, then he can count double the number of steps than actually exist. On the other hand, if he only concentrates on the white outline of the steps then the risers appear to be hanging in the air. Both these effects are the result of the outlines of the treads not going under the outline of the risers.

The Small Samrat Yantra does not only differ from the original type of plastered stone building in its accentuation of the outline of the wall and staircase. A striking structural feature of the instrument is the deliberate contrast of the

In contrast to the down-to-earth use which Muslim mathematicians made of numbers, the Hindus' use of numbers went well beyond counting or calculation. They were always trying to abstract theological knowledge through numerology and to reveal universal correspondences through proportional formulations. Such attempts were based on the conviction encountered in many cultures that there is a mathematically definable correspondence between everything immanent and transcendental.

This concept also found expression in literature devoted to Hindu architecture. There are plenty of declarations about numbers which were supposed to guarantee the ritual purity of a building or the observance of cosmological

146   On the significance of the top view of buildings in Hindu architecture, see the author's *Living architecture: Indian*, New York and London, 1969, p. 138.

relationships, while precise dimensions, information on the building period or building costs are seldom given.

The Muslims, on the other hand, had a high regard for numbers as a means of quantitatively recording their material environment. Babur, the first Mogul, after conquering Hindustan, began to fill up his diary with information on local measuring systems, the division of time and geography.[147] The book *A'in-i akbari*,[148] written on the orders of the Great Mogul Akbar, forms the climax of the emerging trend in the Mogul empire of recording statistically as many areas of life as possible. In the chapter 'About Buildings', not one single palace or mosque is mentioned, but the weights of building materials, the prices of the materials and the wages of the workers are listed in detail.

Since then, there have been calculations of expenditure available for most of India's Muslim buildings, but only very few for Hindu buildings. Jai Singh was an orthodox Hindu and there were no Muslims amongst his collaborators. This explains why there is no information on costs, time and dimensions for the observatories and the town of Jaipur. But let us attempt to draw from contemporary, earlier and later information a picture, albeit a fragmentary one, of the financial aspects of Jai Singh's building activities.

In 1792, J. L. Williams in Benares received from the chairman of the City Council, a certain Nabob Ali Ibrahim Kaun, the following information concerning the salaries of Jai Singh's employees:

The design of the observatory was drawn by Jaggernaut, and executed under the direction of Sadashu Mahajin; but the head-worker was Mahon, the son of Mahon a potmaker of Jeypoor. The pundit's pay was five rupees per day; the workmen's two rupees, besides presents; some got lands, or villages, worth 3 or 400 rupees yearly value; others money.[149]

In Hunter's report, there is some information about the salaries of Jai Singh's astronomers. He gives an account of a pundit not otherwise named, who was the most important adviser of Jaya Sinha in astronomical matters. The Raja conferred the title of court astronomer on him and a fief which brought in 5,000 rupees per annum.[150]

From these sources, the annual income of Jai Singh's employees works out as follows: court astronomer 5,000 rupees per year, architect 1,600 rupees per year, craftsman 940 rupees per year. In comparison, we should quote the wages which the Great Mogul Shah Jahan paid to the architects responsible for the Taj Mahal: master builder 12,000 rupees per year, famous smiths 3,500 rupees per year, local stonemasons 2,400 – 4,500 rupees per year.[151] And from the *A'in-i akbari*, we should also quote the particularly low wages which, so it is said, brought a large part of the craftsmen in Fatehpur Sikri close to starvation: masons 24 rupees per year, carpenters 15 rupees per year, soldiers 120 rupees per year, officers in charge of 1,000 men 8,400 rupees per year (the price of a sheep was 6.5 rupees, and of a duck 1 rupee).[152]

Father Strobl reports that Jai Singh sent him and Father Gabelsperger, as travel expenses, 'a bill of exchange of a thousand rupees (that being about the same as Bavarian guilders)'.[153] This information is particularly useful since it contains the exchange rate with a European currency and thus enables a comparison of contemporary building expenses in India and Bavaria to be made.

In a different account, Strobl also mentions building costs: 'What costs he [Maharaja Jai Singh] is laying out for scholarly buildings [observatories] is plain to see: on the only machine which he invented himself and which was supposed to depict perpetual motion, he has until now spent over fifty thousand guilders.'[154] By the 'machine he invented himself' he presumably means the Great Samrat Yantra of Jaipur.

147 Babur, *Memoirs*, translated into English by Leyden and Erskine, London, 1826.
148 Abul-Fazl, *A'in-i akbari*, new edition, Delhi, 1965.
149 J. L. Williams, 'Further Particulars Respecting the Observatory at Benares', *Philosophical Transactions of the Royal Society of London*, MDCCXCIII, part 1, London, 1793, p. 49.
150 William Hunter, 'Some Accounts of the Astronomical Labours of Jayasinha', in *Asiatic Researches*, vol. 5, 1799.
151 According to M. A. Chaghtai, *Le Tadj Mahal d'Agra*, Brussels, 1938.
152 According to Abul-Fazl, *A'in-i akbari*, new edition, Delhi, 1965.
153 R. P. A. Strobl, *Brieffe aus Ost-Indien*, in *Allerhand so Lehr- als Geistreiche Brieffe, Schriften...*, edited by F. Keller, Vienna, 1758, no. 643, p. 10.
154 Ibid., no. 644, p. 15.

The costs for the whole observatory can thus be estimated at two or three times as much, that is, 100,000 – 150,000 guilders or rupees. This is an enormous sum for the budget of a principality if we consider that Jai Singh had a total of five observatories and a new royal capital built. His building budget was probably only exceeded by that of the emperor who, as an example, laid out the following amounts for the richest palaces, mosques and mausoleums in the Orient: for the Pearl Mosque in the castle of Agra 300,000 rupees,[155] for the Taj Mahal in Agra (without the grounds) 5,000,000 rupees, for the hall for public audiences in the fortress of Delhi 200,000 rupees.[156]

Strobl's astonishment at Jai Singh's enormous outlay is understandable if one considers, as he did, what building projects could have been realized in his native Bavaria with these sums. For example, the so-called Cuvilliés Theatre in Munich (1750 – 53) cost 52,968 Bavarian guilders according to the estimate – roughly as much as the Samrat Yantra – and 169,408 guilders according to the final bill;[157] the parish church in Starnberg (1764) cost 3,586 guilders according to the final estimate.[158]

From such comparisons it can be seen just how rich Jai Singh, one of the many maharajas in the Mogul empire, must have been in comparison with European princes, not to mention the imperial family of the Moguls themselves.

It is not surprising, then, that the fame of Indian palaces and monuments quickly spread to the European courts. Who in Europe would have been able to build a fortress for a total sum of 8.75 million rupees, and in addition a monument to his favourite wife for a total of 13.5 million rupees and a host of sacred buildings of which one in the fortress of Agra cost 300,000 rupees – around 80 times as much as the church in Starnberg?

The Keel Arch

In comparison with Hindu architecture, there are only a few symbolic architectural forms in Islamic architecture. Only the pointed or keel arch of the mihrab, the niche in a mosque indicating the direction of Mecca, is of liturgical significance. In countries to the east of Arabia, the direction of Mecca is not calculated precisely for each place but is accepted as being precisely west. The pointed arch of every prayer mat and every mosque points like an arrow to the point at which the sun sets at the equinoxes. In this simplified orientation, there is a visible need evident in all cultures to place humanity and its works within a cosmic framework, although this orientation is not expressly defined theologically or justified in Islam.

The shape of the curve in Indo-Islamic keel arches has seen many changes during the 700 years of Muslim rule in India. In addition, regional differences make any classification or dating difficult. Nevertheless, the author has taken a precise measurement of a dozen arches in the observatory in Jaipur. With only a few exceptions and small differences, all the arches proved to be designed according to the same geometrical pattern. They are not, like pointed Gothic and Tudor arches, composed of round arches running into each other tangentially, but are formed as follows: construct a right-angled isosceles triangle on the springing; the point of the triangle serves as the point of the intended arch and its legs form the diagonals of two squares whose sides are half the length of the hypotenuse; halve the side (a) of a square and now divide the lower half into as many segments as side (b); you can choose any number of segments; join the corresponding points on (a) divided by two and (b). The straight lines envelop the curve of the keel arch as tangents. This construction only applies to the arches in Jaipur. The attempt to apply it to the keel arches of the Mogul capitals of Agra, Delhi and Fatehpur Sikri was unsuccessful.

155 According to the archaeological report of 1871–92, p. 145.
156 According to tradition, often quoted without reference.
157 Bavarian Castles and Lakes Authorities, Munich.
158 N. Lieb, Munich baroque architect, Munich, 1941.

In Jai Singh's observatories, shallow arches with a slight engraving can sometimes be found. The arches of the instruments were not normally made out of the same material as the masonry – quarrystone – but rather were added on in fired bricks.

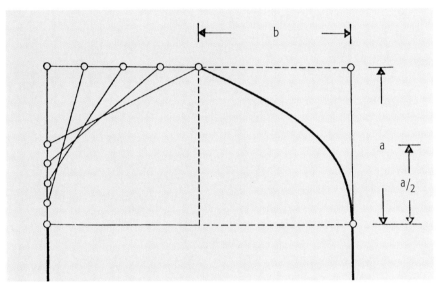

Fig. 139 *Geometrical construction of the keel arch.*

Stone and Masonry Forms

The architectural forms prevalent in India and Persia were strongly influenced by the building materials available. Most of Persia's monumental buildings were constructed in brick covered with tiles and glazed bricks. The ceilings had horizontal wooden beams and the roofs were occasionally topped by tiled domes.

In India, where the local tradition of building in brick ended with the Aryan invasion and the destruction of the Indus Valley culture (Mohenjo Daro and Harappa, 1500 BC), they had built for centuries in bamboo or, from about the 7th century AD, in stone. For sacred buildings, they preferred for theological reasons the above-ground or underground monolithically built

room. As we have seen (see page 117), in these monolithic buildings they often imitated the shapes produced by bamboo building techniques; and later, when ashlar buildings replaced monolithic buildings, they again adopted all the typical features of the earlier monolithic buildings. As a result of this development, volume and interior space were given equal spatial functions.

In Islamic architecture, the wall is merely the shell of the interior space. Or it forms the boundary of the exterior space, as in the courtyard of a caravanserai or a mosque. Only in the double domes does it occasionally form (apparent) volumes in its own right.

Which of the two formal principles determined the design of the observatories? Jagannath himself described a reductive building process in the making of a Jai Prakash Yantra[159] and we remember the Hindu method of creating space by hollowing out a monolith.

On looking at the Jai Prakash Yantra (fig. 51) or the Mishra Yantra (fig. 78), it is the solid volume we think of and not perhaps the wall structures. It is the monolithic Hindu approach and not the Islamic predilection for two-dimensional shapes which appears to predominate. Nevertheless, a glance at the ground plans and sections of all the yantras shows that they are consistently made up solely of walls and frameworks of walls. Only in the case of very small areas of wall did they leave the wall mass untouched. If it was sufficiently large then they broke it up into an arrangement of internal rooms, walls and external rooms. This means that a Hindu-style architectural form was being technically and functionally 'Islamicised'.

The best illustration of this is the Mishra Yantra in Delhi. It would have been consistent with local building traditions to build the whole instrument out of one rock. Historical engravings show that this would have been possible, since at an earlier date low rock formations surrounded the observatory. Instead of this, they supported individual marble circular scales and

159 See *Zig Mohammad Shahi*, translated into English by William Hunter, 'Some Accounts of the Astronomical Labours of Jayasinha', in *Asiatic Researches*, vol. 5, 1799.

measuring poles by a complicated system of quarrystone walls and broke up the whole shape into two storeys, each with two recreation rooms, courtyards and storerooms (figs. 142, 143). This blend of Indian and Islamic spatial concepts makes the Mishra Yantra a typical late example of Indo-Islamic architecture.

Unfortunately, this blend also had a drawback: as a result of phenomena relating to subsidence, which were much less familiar to the Hindu architect thinking monolithically than to the Islamic master mason, almost all of Jai Singh's instruments ended up being useless for measuring purposes. However, given that the yantras were more important as symbolic structures than as instruments, their significance as monumental expressions of the Indo-Islamic architectural style remains undiminished.

Plans 2 | The observatories of Jai Singh
in Benares, built 1737   25°18′25.4″ north
and in Delhi, built 1724   25°37′35″ north

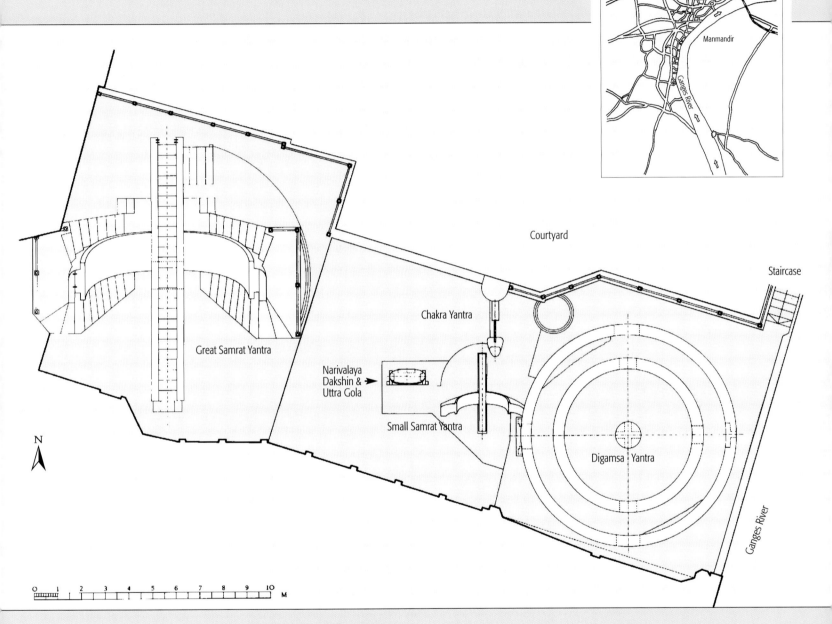

N

Courtyard

Staircase

Chakra Yantra

Great Samrat Yantra

Narivalaya
Dakshin &
Uttra Gola

Small Samrat Yantra

Digamsa Yantra

Ganges River

Varuna River

Manmandir

Ganges River

Fig. 140   *Plan of the observatory on the roof terrace of the Manmandir Palace, Benares.*

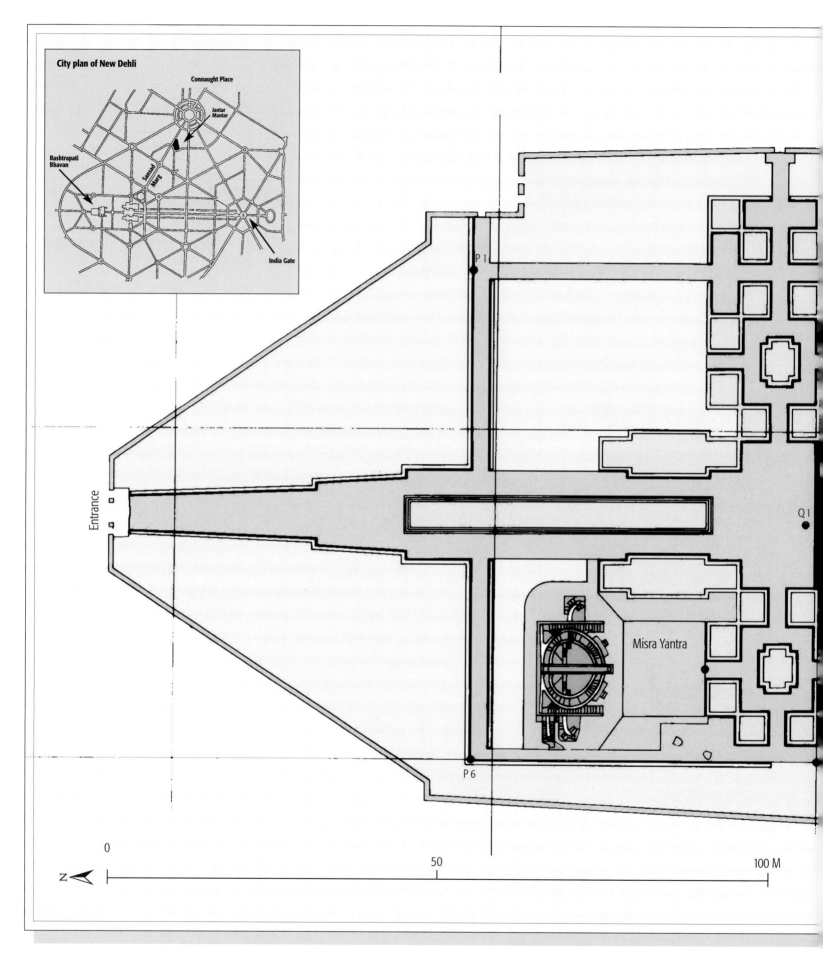

City plan of New Dehli

Connaught Place

Jantar Mantar

Rashtrapati Bhavan

Sansad Marg

India Gate

Entrance

P 1

Q 1

Misra Yantra

P 6

0

50

100 M

N

Fig. 141   Plan of the Jantar Mantar observatory, New Delhi.

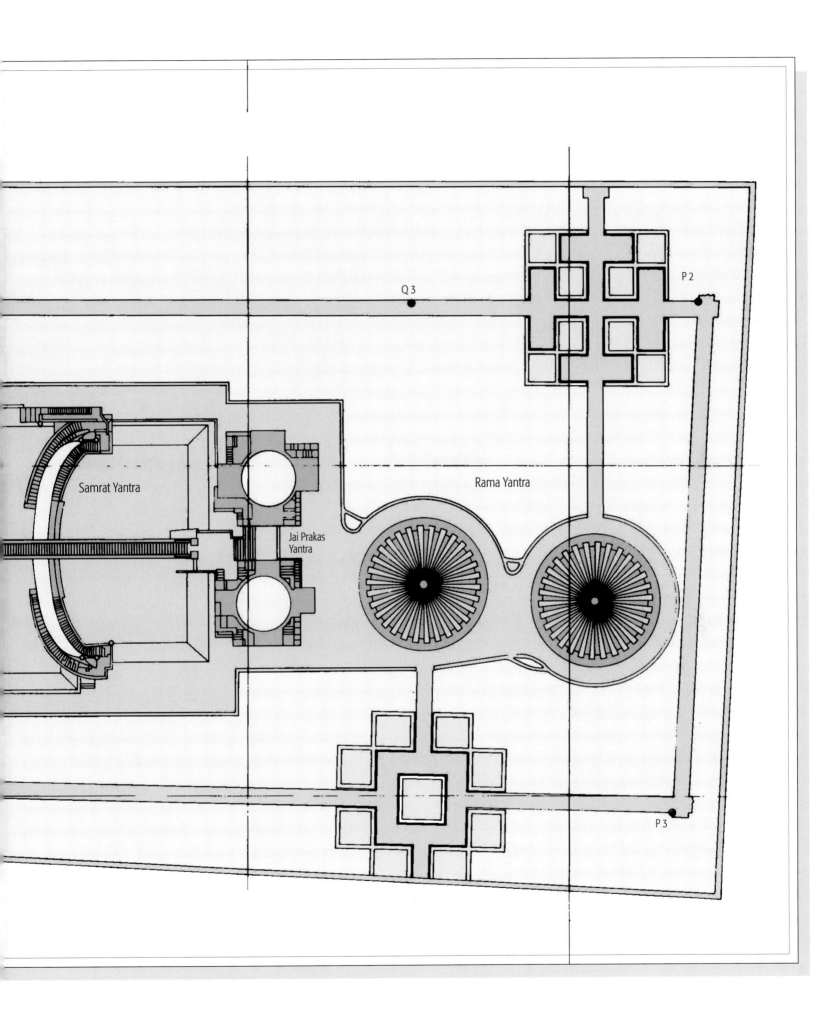

Samrat Yantra

Jai Prakas
Yantra

Rama Yantra

Q 3

P 2

P 3

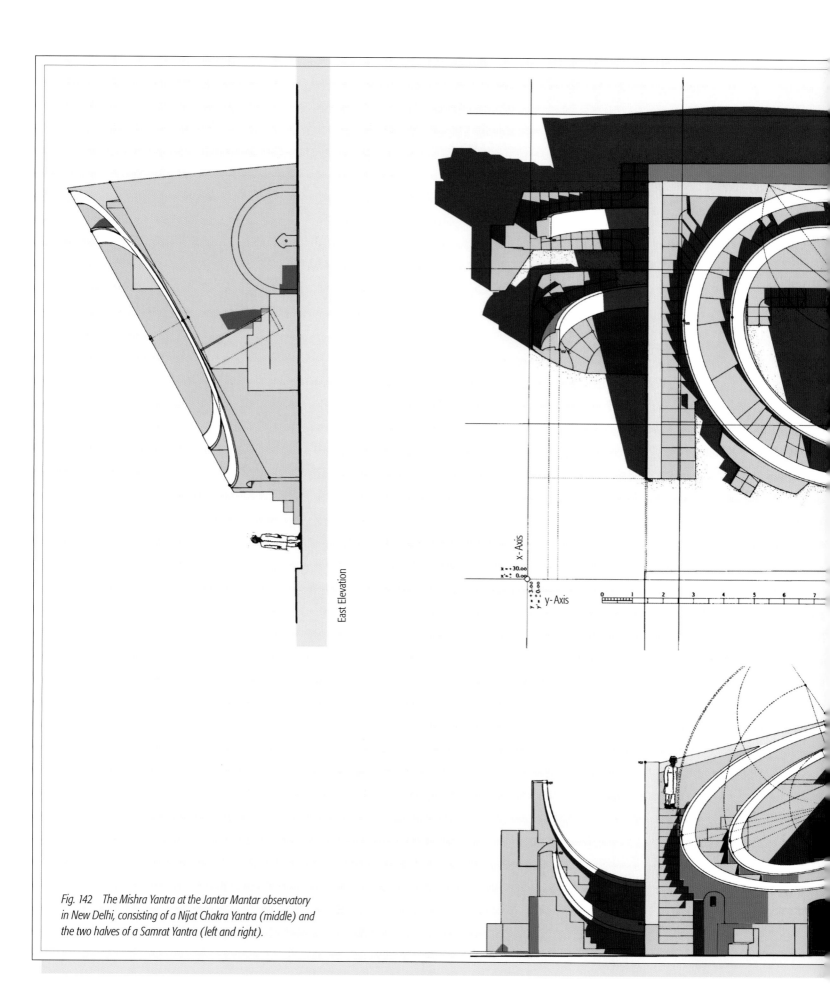

East Elevation

x - Axis

x = -30.00
x' = 0.00

y = -3.00
y' = 0.00

y - Axis

0   1   2   3   4   5   6   7

Fig. 142   The Mishra Yantra at the Jantar Mantar observatory
in New Delhi, consisting of a Nijat Chakra Yantra (middle) and
the two halves of a Samrat Yantra (left and right).

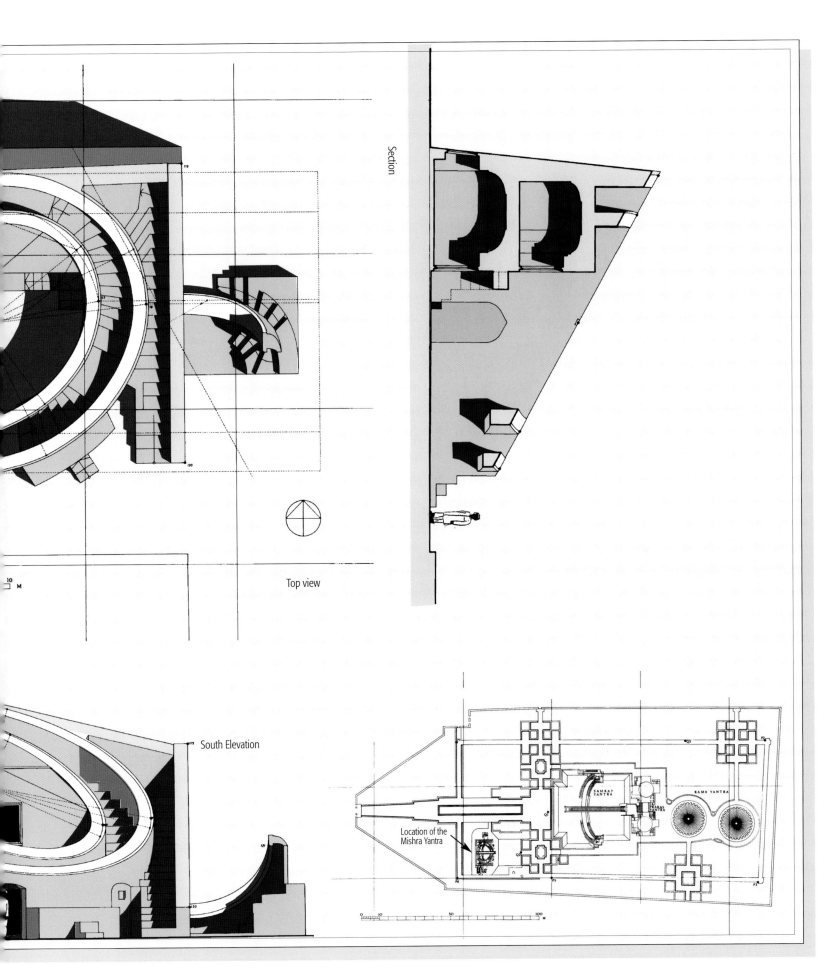

Section

Top view

South Elevation

Location of the
Mishra Yantra

SAMRAT YANTRA

RAMA YANTRA

151

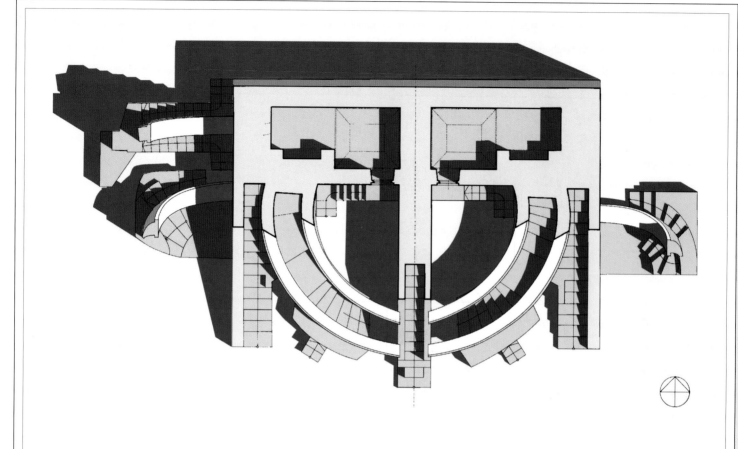

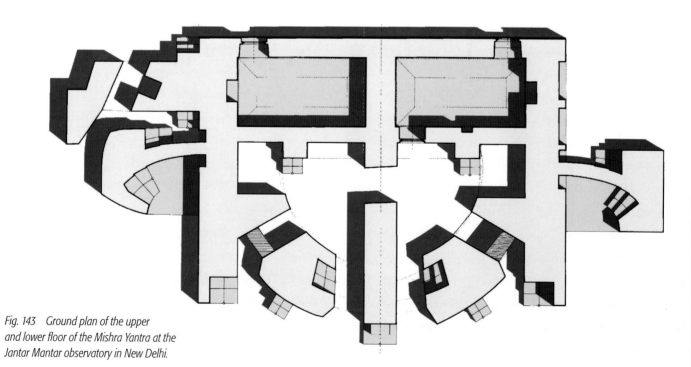

Fig. 143   Ground plan of the upper
and lower floor of the Mishra Yantra at the
Jantar Mantar observatory in New Delhi.

0 1 2 3 4 5 6 7 8 9 10
M

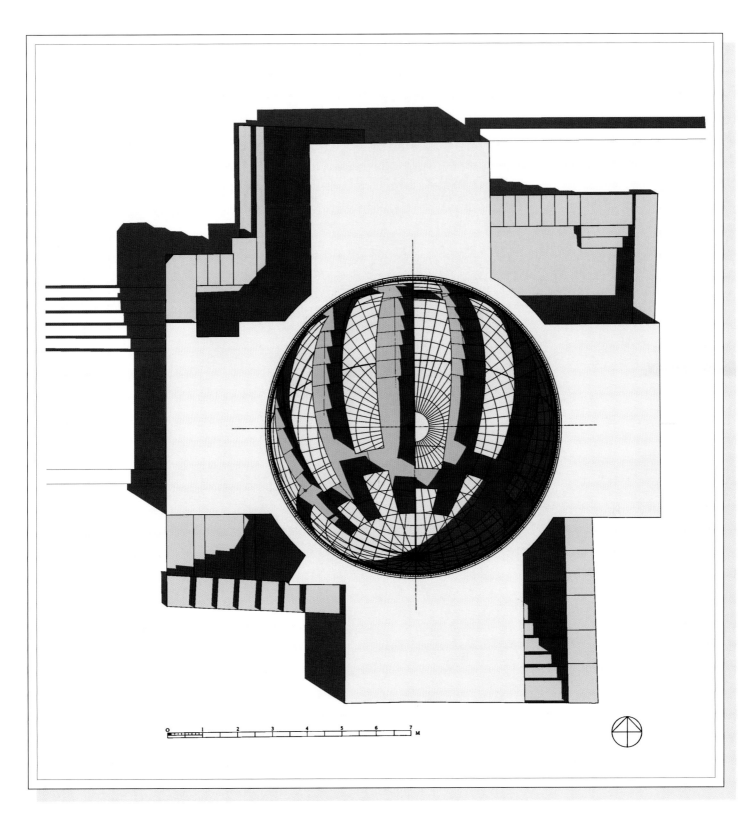

Fig. 144   Top view of the eastern Jai Prakash Yantra at the Jantar Mantar observatory in New Delhi.

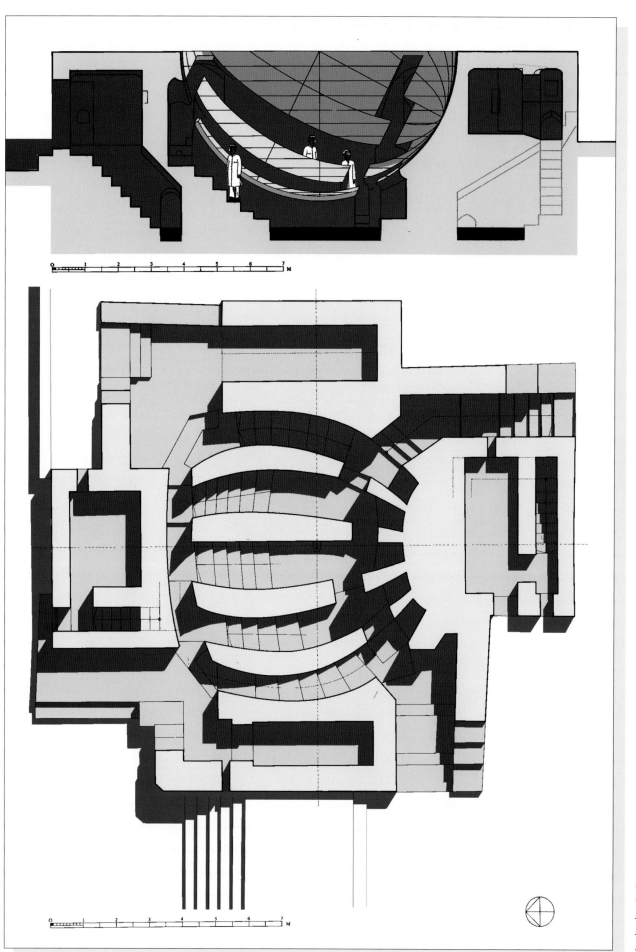

Fig. 145   Ground plan and section of the Eastern Jai Prakash Yantra at the Jantar Mantar observatory in New Delhi.

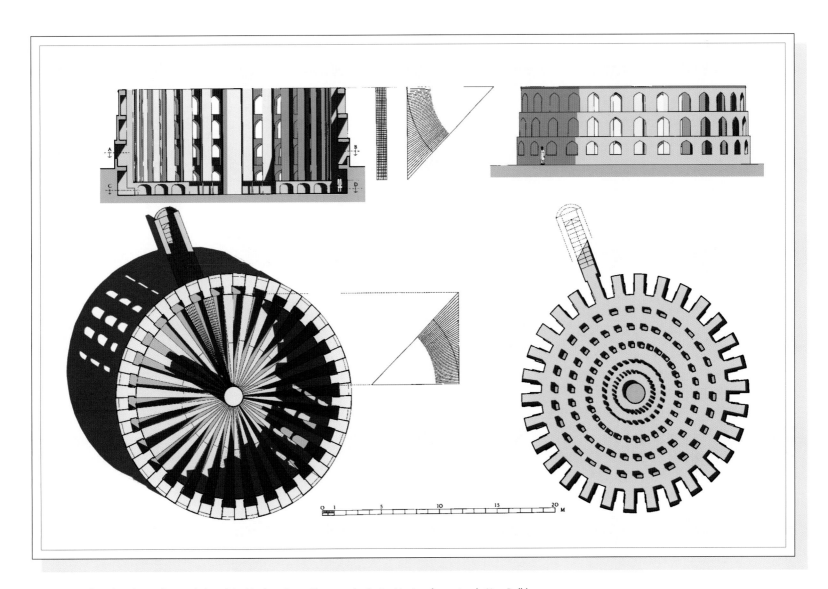

Fig. 146   Section, elevation and ground plan of the Northern Rama Yantra at the Jantar Mantar observatory in New Delhi.

Glossary

- AGNI   Fire, fire god.
- ALIDADE   (Arabian) Observation instrument, index.
- ALTITUDE   The angle between the horizon and a star measured on its vertical circle.
- AZIMUTH   The angle between the south point of the horizon and the intersection with the horizon of the vertical circle of a star.
- CHAKRA   Circle.
- CHAYA   The eaves on the façades of Hindu and Indo-Islamic buildings.
- DAKSHINO BHITTI YANTRA   Meridian wall.
- DECLINATION   Angular distance of a star from the celestial equator, measured along the hour circles of the star.
- DIGAMSA YANTRA   From *dig-ansa,* meaning 'azimuth'. Azimuthal instrument.
- ECLIPTIC   The earth's orbit around the sun, divided into 12 zodiacal signs.
- EQUINOX   The time at which the sun, during its apparent annual movement, stands at the intersection of the ecliptic and the celestial equator, when day and night are of equal length.
- GNOMON   A vertical post casting a shadow; occasionally used instead of a polos.
- GURU   Spiritual adviser.
- HOUR CIRCLE   A great circle of a celestial body on the celestial sphere which passes through the body and the north celestial pole.
- JAI PRAKASH   Hemispherical instrument designed by Jai Singh.
- JAIPUR   *Jai-pur* means 'town of victory'; the royal seat of the Maharaja Jai Singh II, today the regional capital of Rajasthan.
- JANTAR MANTAR   Jantar = yantra, mantar = mantra; magical instrument, magic sign; name for Jai Singh's observatory in Delhi.

- KAPALI YANTRA   *Kapala* means 'hemisphere'; hemispherical-shaped instrument.
- KRANTI WRITTA   *Kranti-writ* means 'declination circle'; occasionally also denotes the ecliptic.
- MAHARAJA   'Great king'; title of a prince.
- MANASARA   Medieval architectural manual.
- MANDALA   Circular or square symbolic representation of the universe.
- MANTRA, MANTRAM   Prayer formula.
- MERCHET   Ancient Egyptian observation instrument.
- MERIDIAN   The great circle of the celestial sphere which passes through the zenith and the nadir of a place of observation and through the celestial poles.
- MERIDIAN PLANE   Plane which passes over the meridian.
- MISHRA YANTRA   Composite instrument.
- MOGULS, GREAT MOGULS   Islamic imperial dynasty in India.
- NARIVALAYA UTTAR GOLA   Equatorial instrument for the northern hemisphere.
- OBLIQUITY OF THE ECLIPTIC   The inclination of the plane of the ecliptic to the plane of the celestial equator (23° 27').
- PADA   Square section of a mandala.
- POLAR ALTITUDE   Angular distance of the celestial pole from the horizon of the place of observation; it is like the geographical latitude of the place of observation.
- POLE STAR   Star lying close to the celestial pole.
- POLOS   A stick pointing to the celestial pole which casts a shadow.
- PRTHIVI   Earth.
- PRIME VERTICAL   The vertical circle passing through the east and west points of the horizon.

- PUNDIT   Brahman title.
- QUADRANT   Quarter circle.
- RAMA YANTRA   Previously Ram Yantra; presumably an instrument named after Maharaja Ram Singh.
- RASHI VALAYA YANTRA   *Rashi-valaya* means 'zodiacal circle'; ecliptical instrument.
- RIGHT ASCENSION   The angle between the vernal point and the point of intersection of the celestial equator with the hour circle of a star.
- SAMRAT YANTRA   Royal instrument: the largest instrument in the observatory.
- SHASTANSHA YANTRA   Sextant.
- SOLSTICE   The two times during the year at which the sun reaches its highest or lowest point in the sky at noon.
- STHAPATI   Hindu priest-architect.
- TANTRA, TANTRAM   Tantric doctrine.
- TRILITHON   Massive megalithic structure composed of three stones, two standing stones and a lintel. The inner circle at Stonehenge contains a number of trilithons.
- VERTICAL CIRCLE   A great circle on the celestial sphere passing from the observer's zenith through a given celestial body.
- YANTRA, YANTRAM   Instrument, tool, diagram, magic sign. Also jantar.
- ZENITH   Point of intersection of a plumb line from the observer's location with the celestial sphere, i.e., the point in the sky directly overhead.
- ZENITH DISTANCE   The angular distance of a star from the zenith. The zenith distance and altitude of a star always make 90°.

Bibliography

HINDU ARCHITECTURE

Acharya, P. K. *An Encyclopedia of Hindu Architecture,* Oxford University Press, 1927–46.

Archaeological Survey of India Annual Reports, Calcutta, New Delhi.

Basham, A. L. *The Wonder that was India,* Bombay, 1963.

Bhattacharyya, T. *The Canons of Indian Art,* Calcutta, 1963.

Boner, A., and S. Rath Sarma. *Silpa Prakasa,* Leiden, 1966.

Bose, N. K. *Orissan Architecture,* Calcutta, 1931.

Brown, P. *Indian Architecture,* Bombay, 1965.

Coomaraswamy, A. K. *History of Indian and Indonesian Art,* New York, 1965.

Diez, E. *Die Kunst Indiens,* Berlin, 1925.

Fabri, Ch. *An Introduction to Indian Architecture,* Bombay, 1963.

Fergusson, J. *History of Indian and Eastern Architecture,* Delhi, 1967.

Fischer, K. *Schöpfungen Indischer Kunst,* Cologne, 1959.

Frederic, L. *L'Inde, ses temples, ses sculptures,* Paris, 1959.

Gangoly, O. C. *Indian Architecture,* Bombay, 1954.

Goetz, H. *Fünf Jahrtausende indischer Kunst,* Baden-Baden, 1959.

Havell, E. B. *Indian Architecture,* London, 1913.

Kramrisch, S. *The Hindu Temple,* 2 vols. University of Calcutta, 1946.

La Roche, E. *Indische Baukunst,* Munich, 1921.

Link, H. *Himmelskörper aus Stein: ein Konzept von Zeit und Raum in einem Kaliyamman Tempel,* Berlin, 1999.

Rambach, P., and V. de Golish. *Indische Tempel und Götterbilder,* Biberach, 1954.

Rowland, B. *The Art and Architecture of India,* London, 1953.

Shukla, D. N. *Hindu Science of Architecture,* vol. 1 of *Vastu Sastra,* Chandigarh, 1960.

Tadgell, Ch. *The History of Architecture in India,* London, 1990.

Volwahsen, A. *Living Architecture: Indian,* New York and London, 1969.

Wu, Nelson. *Architektur der Chinesen und Inder,* New York, 1963.

Zimmer, H. *Kunstform und Yoga im indischen Kultbild,* Berlin, 1926.

—, *Myths and Symbols in Indian Art and Civilization,* Washington, 1947.

—, *The Art of Indian Asia,* Bollingen Series, New York, 1955.

ISLAMIC ARCHITECTURE IN INDIA

Abul-Fazl. *A'in-i akbari,* Delhi, 1965.

Ancient India, Bulletin of the Archaeological Survey of India, New Delhi.

Babur. *Memoirs,* translated into English by Leyden and Erskine, London, 1921.

Brown, P. *Indian Architecture, Islamic Period,* Bombay, 1965.

Chaghtai, M. A. *Le Tadj Mahal d'Agra,* Brussels, 1938.

Fanshawe, N. C. *Delhi, Past and Present,* London, 1902.

Haig, W., and R. Burn. *The Cambridge History of India,* New Delhi, 1963.

Havell, E. B. *Indian Architecture,* London, 1913.

Le Bon, G. *Les Monuments de L'Inde,* Paris, 1893.

Mitchell, G. *The Royal Palaces of India,* London, 1994.

Pascha, F. *Die Baukunst des Islam,* Darmstadt, 1887.

Reuther, O. *Indische Paläste und Wohnhäuser,* Berlin, 1924.

Sharp, H. Delhi, *Its Story and Buildings,* Bombay, 1921.

Smith, E. W. *Portfolio of Indian Architectural Drawings,* London, 1897.

Villiers-Stuart, C. M. *Gardens of the Great Mughals,* London, 1913.

Volwahsen, A. *Living Architecture: Islamic Indian,* New York and London, 1970.

MAHARAJA JAI SINGH II OF JAIPUR AND HIS OBSERVATORIES

Barker, Sir R. 'An Account of the Bramin's Observatory at Benares', in *Philosophical Transactions of the Royal Society of London,* vol. 67, 1777.

Chetwode, P. 'Delhi Observatory, The Paradise of an Early Cubist', *The Architectural Review,* 1935.

Garrett, A., and Ch. Guleri. *The Jaipur Observatory and its Builder,* Allahabad, 1902.

Hunter, W. 'Some Accounts of the Astronomical Labours of Jayasinha', in *Asiatic Researches,* vol. 5, 1799.

Kaye, G. R. *The Astronomical Observatories of Jai Singh,* Calcutta, 1918.

—, *Hindu Astronomy,* Calcutta, 1924.

Keller, F. *Allerhand so lehr- und geistreiche Briefe, Schriften und Reisebeschreibungen, Briefe aus Ostindien,* nos. 641–47, Vienna, 1758.

Noti, S. *Land und Volk des königlichen Astronomer Dschaisingh II. Maharadscha von Dschaipur,* Berlin, 1911.

Rahman, A. *Maharaja Sawai Jai Sing II and Indian Renaissance*, New Delhi, 1987.

Tieffenthaler, J. *Historisch-Geographische Beschreibung Hindustans*, Berlin, 1885.

Tod, J. *Annals and Antiquities of Rajasthan*, vol. 2, London, 1832.

Volwahsen, A. 'Jantar Mantar – Zauberzeichen', in *du-atlantis*, June 1966, Zürich.

—, *Zur Architektur der Sternwarten des Maharaja Jai Singh II von Jaipur*, Ph.D. thesis, Munich, 1969.

Williams, J. L. 'Further Particulars Respecting the Observatory at Benares', *Philosophical Transactions of the Royal Society of London*, London, 1793.

OBSERVATORIES IN GENERAL

Atkinson, R. J. C. *Stonehenge*, London, 1960.

Barthold, W. *Mir Islama, Kritika i bibliografija*, St. Petersburg, 1912.

—, *Ulugh Beg und seine Zeit*, Leipzig, 1935.

Bassermann-Jordan, E. *Geschichte der Zeitmessung*, Berlin, 1920.

Biot, M. J.-B. 'Détermination de l'équinoxe vernal de 1853', in *Astronomie égyptienne*, Paris, 1855.

Borchardt, L. *Alte ägyptische Zeitmessung*, Berlin, 1920.

—, *Längen und Richtungen der vier Grundkanten der Großen Pyramide bei Gise*, Berlin, 1926.

Brahe, T. *Tychonis Brahe Dani Opera Omnia*, edited by J. L. E. Dreyer, 15 vols. Copenhagen, 1913–29; reprinted Amsterdam, 1972.

Hawkins, G. S. *Stonehenge Decoded*, New York, 1965.

Leonov, N. *Naucnyi podrig samarkandskich astronomov*, XV, Moscow, 1960.

Morley, S. G. *The Ancient Maya*, Stanford, 1956.

Needham, J. *Chinese Astronomy and the Jesuit Mission*, London, 1958.

Parker, R. *The Calendars of Ancient Egypt*, Chicago, 1950.

Schoy, K. *Gnomonik der Araber*, Berlin, 1923.

Sédillot, L. A. *Mémoire sur les instruments astronomiques des Arabes*, Paris, 1844.

—, *Prolégomènes des tables astronomiques d'Oloug-Beg*, vols. 1 and 2, Paris, 1847.

Repsold, J. A. *Zur Geschichte der astronomischen Meßwerkzeuge 1450–1830*, Leipzig, 1908.

Ricketson, Jr, O. G., and E. B Ricketson. *Uaxactun, Guatemala, Group E. 1926–1931*, Carnegie Institution of Washington, publ. no. 477, 1937.

Stierlin, H. *Maya, Architektur der Welt*, Fribourg, 1964.

Vitruvius, *De Architectura*, translated by Joseph Gwilt, London, 1826.

Vjatkin, V. L. *Izvestija Russkago Komiteta dlja izucenija Srednej i Vostocnoj Azii Serija II*, no. 1, p. 76–93.

Zinner, E. *Die Geschichte der Sternkunde*, Berlin, 1931.

—, *Deutsche und niederländische astronomische Instrumente*, Munich, 1967.

SYMBOLISM AND ARCHITECTURAL FORM

Bacon, E. *Design of Cities*, London, 1967.

Boner, A. *Principles of Composition in Hindu Sculpture*, Leiden, 1962.

Fuller, B. *Structure in Art and Science*, Vision and Value series, Studio Vista, London, 1965.

Jung, C. G. *Aion*, in *Collected Works of C. G. Jung*, vol. 9, Princeton University Press, 1969.

—, *Commentary on 'The Secret of the Golden Flower'*, in *Collected Works of C. G. Jung*, vol. 13, Princeton University Press, 1967.

—, *Configurations of the Unconscious*, in *Collected Works of C. G. Jung*, vol. 18, Princeton University Press, 1977.

Kepes, G. *Vision and Value series*, Studio Vista, London, 1965.

Kepler, J. *Mysterium Cosmographicum*, Graz, 1596.

—, *Harmonices Mundi*, Linz, 1619.

Le Corbusier. *Le Modulor, Modulor 2*, English edition, Birkhauser, 2000.

Madec, Ph. *Etienne-Louis Boullée*, Basel, Boston and Berlin, 1989.

Mumford, L. *The City in History*, New York, 1989.

Saraswati, Swami P. *The Yantram*, Calcutta, n.d.

The architecture of the palace at Jaipur harks takes on the forms of the imperial Mogul palaces in Dehli.

Photographic Credits